D0065563

THE WORLD OF CONCIERGE MEDICINE

How a Renaissance in Health Care Can Help You and Your Loved Ones Live Long and Healthy Lives

RUSS ALAN PRINCE

DANIEL CARLIN, MD

JOHN J. BOWEN JR.

The World of Concierge Medicine
How a Renaissance in Health Care Can Help You and Your Loved Ones Live Long and Healthy Lives

By Russ Alan Prince, Daniel Carlin, MD, and John J. Bowen Jr.

AES Nation • www.aesnation.com

To Jeff and Jeff,

my original concierge physicians

—*Russ*

To my dad,

the original concierge physician to the entire town of
Dalton, Massachusetts

—*Dan*

To the concierge physicians who've made a
huge difference in my life

—*John*

Table of Contents

PROLOGUE

From Central Asia to the High Seas to a Health Care Renaissance

Dan's story

It was early morning as my team and I paced through our mud-walled compound, part of the Nasir Bagh Refugee Resettlement #4. Located halfway between Peshawar and the Khyber Pass, the camp was the first and, for thousands of Afghan refugees fleeing the Russian invasion of Afghanistan, the only stop. As medical director of the camp clinic, I was tasked with providing the best possible care for our patients—a tall order in that chaotic environment.

Like every morning, we triaged hundreds of patients, selecting the 50 or 60 sickest among them. Our patients needed our help in almost everything, but especially in pediatrics, orthopedics, OB-GYN, trauma and infectious disease. The common diseases in the camp were both medieval and brand new to me—polio, leprosy and every form of tuberculosis possible. Despite my years of medical training and practice—including a stint in the U.S. Navy as the only doctor aboard a guided missile cruiser with a crew of 600—I had little experience in these diseases' diagnosis and treatment.

This came to a sharp point that day in a tragic case that, even 30 years later, I still think about often: A 12-year-old girl wrapped in a worn blue towel was brought in by her mother for recurrent seizures. Small for her age and wasted by starvation, she was a new arrival from across the border. Her name was Sher Gul (which means "lion flower"). We stopped the seizures with IV Valium, but Sher Gul's rigidly stiff neck gave away the cause: advanced bacterial meningitis. Despite antibiotics and evermore increasing doses of Valium, she grew worse.

My team and I tried to call for help from an infectious disease expert back in New York. The 13-hour time difference and an overloaded, antiquated rural Pakistani phone system made the situation almost impossible. By the time we heard from our expert, Sher Gul had been dead for two days. Burnt into my memory is the sight of her elderly uncle picking up her lifeless body and walking out of our clinic to return her to her family across the camp.

Flash forward a decade to 1998. After additional years of training and practice in emergency medicine, I founded WorldClinic, a telemedicine practice originally focused on ships at sea. I knew from my Navy service what a challenging environment a ship could be, and I was fortunate that the Internet was moving from academia to the mainstream at this time. Very quickly, I got the chance to use the Internet to make medical history.

It was during the Around Alone Race, an eight-month competition for solo sailors racing to circumnavigate the globe, for which I was serving as medical director. Viktor Yazykov, a solo sailor and former Russian commando, had developed a large, deep tissue hematoma in his left arm. Over the course of three days, it had become dangerously infected. At the time, he was 900 miles west of Cape Town, South Africa, and we had lost voice communication with him. In a rapid-fire exchange of satellite-based emails, he described his symptoms. It was immediately clear that he needed surgery to open the pocket of infection and successfully drain it, and then to control the associated bleeding and start antibiotics.

In a 16-step email, I instructed him on the procedure. Without any anesthesia, he performed it perfectly, saving his arm and most likely his life in the process. Within three days, the story of an email-enabled lifesaving surgical procedure had been picked up by hundreds of newspapers and television news shows. For a while, both Viktor and I experienced what it felt like to be an overnight news sensation.

This case proved the value of telemedicine, but it was still too far beyond the mainstream since the Internet was only just beginning to take hold. In response, I pivoted WorldClinic toward the concierge telemedicine practice it is today.

In the first phase of WorldClinic, we focused completely on dealing with unpredictable risk by acting as a "virtual emergency room" to our members worldwide. Our first commercial clients were super yachts and, soon thereafter, the high-net-worth families that owned the boats and wanted WorldClinic to care for their families on a worldwide, anytime, anywhere basis. Some of these families eventually began to hire us into their portfolio companies to care for their senior executives and business travelers.

At the same time, our original high-net-worth family members were aging, and with advances in medical care they began looking for better ways to live longer and healthier lives. Their interest motivated us to research and develop the cutting-edge assessment tools and protocols that we now call *longevity planning*.

Our strategy has been to employ simple personal technology, like smart-phones, to track the key data points in a member's longevity plan—a plan that enables the member to live considerably longer and more vibrantly than would have been possible even just a decade ago.

Our next natural iteration was to address patients' inherent predictable risk by examining things like family history, biomarkers and genome to acquire clues about what a person's future health likely held. In 2016, we created a tightly managed lifetime plan for maximal longevity for our patients. The basis of this plan is the predictive risk revealed by their genome. We take genomic data and convert it into a personal medical protocol for nutrition, key supplements, medications, specific lab and diagnostic tests, and lifestyle changes.

Though we are only at the beginning of this effort, it's obvious already that this approach has far-reaching implications and, if history is any in-dicator, will rapidly spread to all segments of society. By creating a new means to live a longer, healthier life, we are also creating a paradigm for all of us to do so. We are setting the groundwork for a new and better kind of health care, one that will someday be employed by all.

From treating some of the world's neediest in a dusty refugee camp in Pa-kistan to pioneering telemedicine at the dawn of the Internet to creating protocols that promise to extend life spans, I have been privileged to be part of a health care renaissance.

Now I'm privileged to share some of my knowledge with you. In these pages, you will discover how concierge medicine, coupled with cut-ting-edge innovations to increase longevity, can change your life and the lives of your loved ones. And I'm pleased to have as my co-authors two experts in managing the wealth you need to support a long, healthy and productive life: Russ Alan Prince and John Bowen.

Russ and John's story

In more than seven combined decades working with the affluent and advisors to the affluent, we have had thousands of in-depth conversations with wealthy individuals about their most important goals. Overwhelmingly, these goals are not financial at all. Instead, they are about taking care of their families, about making a difference in the world and about living long and healthy lives. Their most precious asset is not money; it's their health and the health of their loved ones.

It only makes sense, then, that a large and growing percentage of the wealthy has adopted concierge medicine. They are willing and able to pay for better, more mobile and more accountable health care.

This is not a new phenomenon: The wealthy have often been the original donors and, in some cases, the first guinea pigs for medical breakthroughs. Cardiac bypass surgery would not have been possible without its first donor, nor would the rapid adoption of bone marrow stem cell replacement after chemotherapy have become a widespread cancer treatment.

Concierge medicine—and in particular its focus on longevity planning— is intensely aligned with the goals and priorities of the wealthy. It gives them much more than extra productive years on Earth; it also helps protect their legacies of wealth and philanthropy. If family members live a longer life, they are better able to act as mentors, maintain family dynamics and provide governance so that they can better preserve their legacy longer.

This is where health care intersects with wealth management. Preserving one's wealth to the end of life—or beyond, when there is a desire to pass on a legacy—has always required astute planning. When longevity planning adds decades to the lives of family members, an even higher level of planning and the use of innovative financial and legal strategies are often needed.

Here we draw on our experience in working with the wealthy, the ultra-wealthy and the Super Rich—those people with a net worth of $500 million or more—as well as with the family offices that serve these families. John brings to the table more than 26 years as a financial advisor to the affluent, along with nearly two decades of coaching both financial advisors and financial institutions in providing world-class service to their affluent clients.

Russ has conducted many dozens of empirical studies on the affluent over the past three decades, and has relayed his results in more than 50 books and hundreds of white papers, articles and blogs. For the past 15 or so years, he has also consulted extensively with ultra-wealthy families and their teams of highly skilled professional advisors around the globe. It would be difficult to find someone with greater insight into the world of the wealthy.

Through our work, we are privy to the powerful systems and solutions the very wealthy use to grow and protect their wealth—and have many times helped implement them. And in recent years, we have witnessed the move of many wealthy families to concierge medicine. We've seen how they are using it to protect their most precious assets and ensure long and productive lives. We've even become members of concierge medicine practices ourselves.

Now we are pulling back the curtain on this exclusive world. We want you to have the same level of financial security and sense of confidence in your health care that the wealthiest among us enjoy.

With this goal in mind, we'll provide you with perspectives on concierge medicine that will help you decide if it makes sense for you and your loved ones. Along the way, we'll prompt you to ask yourself important questions about your preferences in managing both your health and your wealth to help you take the right steps forward.

CHAPTER 1

The Promise of Concierge Medicine

There is a paradigm shift underway in the delivery of high-quality primary health care. There is a sea change in the science of prolonging a person's life. And there is a rebirth of the patient-physician relationship. Concierge medicine has helped bring about all of these remarkable changes.

Independent from third-party reimbursement payment structures, concierge medicine opens a pathway for better preventive health care that can embrace new technology and leverage connectivity to monitor chronic illness and support positive lifestyle changes. Concierge medicine can also incorporate the latest advances into clinical practice, like biomarkers and genomics—two things that insurance will usually not pay for but that have a profound effect on longevity. With concierge medicine, health care can deliver on its ultimate promise: *preventing illness before it even starts.*

Concierge medicine, while not inherently new, has moved from being an outlier of sorts into the mainstream—a trend that will probably dramatically intensify over the next few years. In addition, many aspects of

One hour after rear-ending another car in rural Colorado, the driver began complaining of mild neck pain and tingling in his right thumb and index finger. His spouse called and talked with an on-duty emergency physician at their concierge medical practice. In a five-minute interview conducted via a smartphone Skype link, she described the situation and then carried out a simple guided physical exam that confirmed the possibility of a significant nerve injury.

The emergency physician immediately guided her in immobilizing her husband's neck and arranged transportation to a designated hospital with a verified CT scanner and a qualified radiological team. The physician contacted the emergency room in advance and relayed his concerns, requesting an immediate CT scan of the husband's spine. It revealed a fracture of the fourth cervical vertebra, which was soon stabilized with a rigid neck brace. The patient made a full recovery and suffered no permanent neurological damage.

concierge medicine will become normative and integrated into the traditional health care system. For example, ongoing monitoring of chronic conditions using smartphone-enabled systems will become increasingly common.

Concierge medicine now plays an important role in the lives of a sizable and growing number of people, even if it's just about eliminating the "what to do" anxiety in case of a medical emergency. Moreover, there are stronger and stronger indications that the field of concierge medicine is going to considerably expand.

Given the promise of concierge medicine, you should ask yourself two very important questions:

1. Should my family and I become patients of a concierge medical practice?

2. If so, how do we choose the right practice?

To help you answer these questions, we will provide you with an overview of exactly what concierge medicine is and how it differs from the traditional health care system. Then we'll break down the various types of concierge medical practices and how each manages the range of medical conditions. Next, we will explore the intriguing field of longevity planning and how concierge medical practices are on the leading edge of efforts to extend the human life span.

To help you put your medical care in the context of your financial picture, we'll examine the role of concierge medicine in the rarefied world of family offices and wealth management, and the implications of a potentially longer life span for managing your wealth. Then we will delve into the ways in which concierge medicine is expected to evolve over the coming years and how these changes may affect you. Finally, we'll offer a practical guide for choosing the medical concierge practice that is optimal for you and your family.

Sprinkled throughout these pages you will find numerous stories and case examples, all of them of WorldClinic patients. (All these stories are real, but identifying details have been removed to protect patient privacy.) These vivid illustrations will bring to life the deep and meaningful impact concierge medicine can have on the health of patients—and potentially your and your family's health.

Food for thought

As you think about the quality of the health care you and your loved ones have received over the years, consider these questions:

Are you very confident that, going forward, you'll be able to access high-quality physicians when you need them?

How confident are you that you'll be able to receive cutting-edge medical care?

How confident are you that your physicians will be truly engaged and 100 percent committed to your well-being?

If you have any doubts at all, you should seriously consider the alternative. Let's get started exploring the world of concierge medicine.

CHAPTER 2

Your Most Precious Assets

There's a famous saying: "When you have your health, you have many problems. When you don't have your health, you have but one problem."

This idea applies to everyone, but especially the people you love and care about.

It doesn't matter how rich, famous or well-connected you are, when you're sick or injured, all you want is to be healthy. And most people want the same thing for their children, spouse, other family members and friends.

In life, ill health—at some point—is inevitable. Even the most careful individuals have accidents. Diseases—from cancer and strokes to neurological disorders and severe infections—can beset anyone. There is no way to absolutely avoid health care problems and crises. However, as we'll discuss when we address longevity planning, there are ways to mitigate some of the negative possibilities.

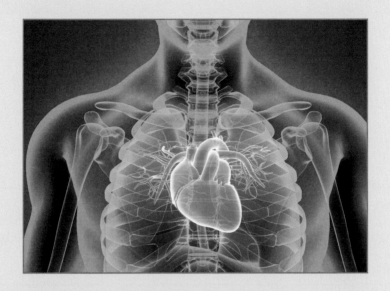

A 55-year-old business owner completes his executive physical, but given this patient's family history of early heart disease, a special panel of cardiac biomarkers was added to the standard exam. Though the exam results were entirely normal, the biomarkers revealed an ongoing vascular injury and the beginning of arterial plaque formation. Under the guidance of a consulting cardiologist with his concierge medical practice, the business owner's blood pressure and cholesterol medications were changed, and the probable culprit, dairy fat, was eliminated from his diet—to the chagrin of the business owner. The biomarker panel was repeated 120 days later, and all evidence of the active vascular injury was resolved. Follow-up blood work, taken twice a year, indicated sustained success in mitigating this long-term risk.

Let's agree that your health and the health of the people you care about are your *most* precious assets, or at least very high on your list. This being the case, consider this question:

How confident are you in getting the highest-quality medical care when you or your loved ones need it?

Who do you want to depend on?

Most people would agree that the traditional health care system in the United States is broken. There is an abundance of issues plaguing it, and one example is Medicare. Created in 1965, it was designed at a time when hospital-based procedures were uncommon and most health care happened at the office level.

Medicare's original objective was to help people pay for expensive, hospital-based treatments, like surgeries, which were less common at the time. This approach to health care created massive financial incentives for hospital-based care (as opposed to preventive care). Now, more than 90 million people are in the "health care years"—age 65 and older. At this time in their lives, when preventive medicine is most important, they are actually more likely to be over-tested and underdiagnosed, and are often significantly less healthy than those whose health care plans have been more prevention-centered. Clearly, a significant failing of the U.S. health care system is that it is not based on simple, consistent prevention, but rather on the complex diagnostics and procedures of hospital-based care.

The rise of hospital-based care has also fostered the age of "seven-minute medicine," where primary care doctors have only a short period to capture a problem and cannot get to know each patient's context (often the true root of the issue) or the patient himself or herself. At best, this is rushed and ineffective triage. This model places no onus on the physician to track the patient's progress and ensure an optimal outcome. The result is a missed opportunity to prevent or effectively treat health care problems before they worsen into crises.

Additionally, with only seven minutes to evaluate a problem, there is now a broad practice of "defensive medicine" among primary care physicians who are substituting excessive testing and referrals to make up for a lack of actual clinical information gathering. Generally speaking, defensive medicine is bad medicine. It's often more concerned with limiting liability for malpractice claims than actually caring for the patient. By subjecting the patient to excessive diagnostic testing and multiple specialist referrals, the primary care physician effectively sheds all professional responsibility for the care of the patient.

Though startling, the phenomenon makes perfect sense in the age of seven-minute medicine, where the typical primary care physician has really only two options:

1. Prescribe a new drug and hope the patient gets better.

2. In even slightly complex cases, make a referral, which spells the end of his or her responsibility for and relationship with the patient.

Ultimately, the net result is that no physician feels personally obligated to ensure the long-term well-being of the patient.

Across the board, from emergency centers to overworked family physicians to medical complexes, there's a lack of physician-patient continuity. This lack of continuity means that several major aspects of effective health care are lost:

- **Loss of access.** Patients are unable to see their physicians quickly or depend on getting their calls returned in a timely manner. Walls of support staff may prevent patients from accessing their physicians.

- **Loss of a holistic approach.** With no single physician or physician team responsible for patients and their progress, care becomes fragmented, with no one consolidating test results, and different specialists working on the same patient without talking to each other. In addition, patient care can become driven by the billing model that creates the most income for the hospital, resulting in some patients' being over-tested and underdiagnosed.

- **Loss of informational continuity.** Once physicians make referrals, they may consider patients to be out of their scope of expertise, and thus do not track the progress of these people. In effect, patients become completely responsible for their own care. These patients will often "doctor shop" to find a new specialist themselves if they are referred to a doctor who does not provide them with a good outcome. This new physician may be outside their usual health system, meaning that few or no medical records get back to their primary care physician. If their condition gets resolved, they will go back to their old health system without transferring their new medical records. Their old health system will now not have the records documenting their recent care success.

Overall, in many respects, the current U.S. health care system has fostered the loss of the individual physician's personal sense of duty to care for his or her patients. Many patients no longer have strong interpersonal relationships with specific primary care physicians. This is the case for almost all types of conventional, hospital-based primary care practices.

The U.S. is not alone in the limitations of its health care system. International health care systems are sometimes idealized. At times, they have been held up as the template that the U.S. health care system should emulate. Although there is cutting-edge medicine taking place outside the U.S. in places like the United Kingdom, Japan and Germany, access is limited and the quality of specialists varies tremendously. Let's consider some of the problems with the health care systems in two other countries.

The Canadian health care system

Although the Canadian health care system may be cited as a success, it often delivers inadequate medical care. There are two major issues with the system.

First, there can be massive delays in higher-level (specialist) care because of the single-payer system structure. While the single-payer system does make preventive care more accessible, it has drastically reduced the number of specialists available. The single-payer system has also raised the patient-to-physician ratio, especially for specialists. As a result, a substantial number of Canadian physicians leave Canada to work internationally because they can be more highly paid abroad.

Second, patients must pay out of pocket if they seek care outside their province, which limits their access to specialists. Even if the best hospital for a specific condition exists in Canada, Canadian citizens who live outside that hospital's province must pay the costs out of pocket to receive care there.

Though wealthy Canadians (and wealthy individuals from other countries) will selectively come to the U.S. for health care, this poses another challenge. Hospital "liaisons" (hospital employees who both target new, high-net-worth donors and ensure the quality of their experience) will often identify these individuals as potential donors and board members. They then become reluctant to direct these patients to any hospital other than their own for care since they do not want to lose a potential donor. In short, wealth gives these individuals access to health care, but not necessarily the quality assurance they are seeking.

The United Kingdom health care system

The U.K. is like Canada in that it has the problems associated with single-payer systems: long delays in hospital-based care; hard rules about the use of resources, such as advanced testing equipment and emerging treatments; and limits on the number of hip and knee replacements and other advanced procedures that can be given each year. And compared to the U.S., the U.K. is, in some ways, obsolescent. For example, immunotherapy is a common cancer therapy in the U.S. but is not yet widely available in the U.K.

The U.K. has more private hospitals, but again these give access while potentially sacrificing quality. For example, many private hospitals exist within larger public hospitals. This relationship incentivizes the private clinic/hospital to refer its patients only within its parent health system, even if specialists better suited for a patient's condition are at a different hospital. (The presence and accompanying issues of private hospitals also exist throughout Western Europe.)

These are some of the problems patients must face because of the potentially severe limitations of health care systems. The real question is, *"Who do you want to depend on?"*

If you have the choice, do you want to depend on a primary care physician or a hospital that is intertwined in the bureaucratic health care morass? Or would you prefer to work with primary care physicians who are free from conflicts of interest and concerned about your health and the health of your loved ones?

Why do people sign up for concierge medicine?

With the problems of our traditional health care system acting as a backdrop, there are four primary reasons people become patients of concierge medical practices. Consider how each may apply to you:

1. **You need to better deal with a current health care concern for yourself or loved ones.** Nearly all of us and our loved ones will at some point be diagnosed with a serious or complex condition. Your first question will probably be *"Where is the best care?"* If your experience with the mainstream health system has been less-than-satisfactory, you are likely looking for better options and well-grounded

second opinions. You need physicians who are truly committed to your health and will act as health care advocates for you in dealing with specialists and medical facilities.

2. **You are uncomfortable with the quality of the traditional primary medical care.** Though you may not have yet experienced a serious problem, you recognize the considerable limitations of the traditional primary care medical system. You want to make sure you have high-caliber physicians and medical facilities for yourself and your loved ones available whenever the need arises.

3. **Your primary care physician is transitioning his or her practice to concierge medicine.** While there are sometimes financial incentives for established physicians to become concierge medical physicians, their core motivation tends to be the ability to deliver superior patient care. These physicians are antagonistic to seven-minute and assembly-line medicine. They want to do what they believe is best for their patients, which many times conflicts with insurance reimbursements and third-party revenue models. In becoming a patient, you recognize the value of joining a concierge medical practice.

4. **You want to live a very long and healthy life and want the same for your loved ones.** Advances in medicine are increasingly extending life spans, a trend that is likely to accelerate. Proactively taking steps to live a long life without illness is called longevity planning. Unfortunately, longevity planning is rarely included in the traditional health care system, though many concierge medical practices are beginning to adopt this approach as the basis of their overall care model.

It's no coincidence that patients who join a concierge medical practice because of a need to get better medical care or their dissatisfaction with the traditional health care system also tend to gravitate toward longevity planning whenever possible. The same is the case for patients who follow their physicians as they transition to concierge medical practices.

Food for thought

There are serious problems with health care systems in the United States and other countries. Moreover, primary care medicine is unlikely to get better. The solution for a great many individuals and families is—if possible—concierge medicine.

You can look at concierge medicine as a way to meaningfully invest in your health and the health of the people you deeply care about. These may be your goals:

- A high-quality lifestyle with the ability to live life to the fullest

- A longer and more productive life where you are actively involved in your own health

- Feeling good and having plenty of energy every day

- Being there for the people you love

A good starting point as you begin to consider the possibility for you and your family is to ask yourself these questions:

What are your most precious assets?

What are you doing to protect them?

CHAPTER 3

What Is Concierge Medicine?

With health care institutions throughout the world increasingly stressed, people with the needed financial resources are increasingly inclined to not rely on these public systems—at least not in the ways most people rely on them. Instead, these individuals and families are more and more able and likely to pay for a higher—if not always an exceptional—standard of health care. The term for this is *concierge medicine* or *concierge health care.*

Concierge medicine is an umbrella term used to describe several different retainer arrangements between a primary care physician and a patient. All the various forms of concierge medicine represent a return to privatizing primary health care. It's a way to get a higher quality of care where you and your loved ones are center stage and *stay* center stage.

In many situations, the most critical benefit of being a patient of a concierge practice is your ability to spend time with the physician. It's *not* any version of assembly-line medicine, which has come to dominate many quarters of primary care. A high-caliber physician's ability to spend time

A 6-year-old girl with a history of peanut allergies was out with her 18-year-old nanny. After the child ate a lunch of French fries and chicken fingers, her nanny noticed the child's lips starting to swell. Within three minutes, the child was having a difficult time breathing. Tapping the family's concierge medical practice's app on her iPhone, the nanny contacted the practice's on-call emergency physician. Using a FaceTime link, the on-duty physician guided the nanny on how to use the child's EpiPen.

The local EMS was also mobilized to assist. Eight hours later, the child was released from the local hospital to the custody of the summoned parents. The cause of the allergic reaction: Peanut oil had been accidentally mixed into the batter for the chicken fingers.

with you means there's a stronger possibility that he or she will avoid errors or the need to take shortcuts that might prove ineffective.

When it comes to concierge medicine, we can distinguish between *assurance* and *insurance*:

- **Assurance** is the security of knowing a talented, knowledgeable physician or other health care professional will answer your calls and provide direction so you can obtain the medical care you need.

- **Insurance**, in contrast, is where you are part of a risk pool and your objective is to cover a percentage of your health care expenses. This means that, for most people, concierge medicine is in addition and complementary to health insurance.

With concierge medicine, you pay for medical expertise, but there are usually additional costs for your care. Laboratory tests such as blood work and diagnostic tests such as MRIs and CAT scans are usually additional costs. When these are not covered by health insurance, patients of concierge medical practices generally pay these costs out of pocket. In many cases, the concierge practice will process payment claims through your insurance.

Taking perspective

Until relatively recently, the delivery of primary medical care was pretty much a cottage industry. It was dominated by a plethora of entrepreneurs—mostly physicians—all running their own practices. They were in control and could care for their patients as they saw fit.

Many physicians tend to date their loss of control to the Medicare and Medicaid legislation of the mid-1960s. Many physicians and health care policy experts see this as the start of the shift in medical decision-making from physicians to administrators. Over time, medical care became increasingly led by MBAs rather than MDs.

This transformation has forced physicians to practice medicine in ways that do not always conform to what they feel is best for the patient. Within this paradigm, it became a necessity for many physicians to adopt the practice of "defensive medicine." More and more tests were being ordered to protect themselves and their careers.

At the same time, patients may not be getting the level of care they want or need. For example, office visits are becoming shorter and shorter and wait times for appointments are becoming longer and longer. More critically, there is frequently a lack of communication between the primary care physicians and the various specialists participating in a patient's care.

Many primary care physicians thus feel they are on a medical practice treadmill—running faster and going nowhere. There are numerous reasons many physicians are disenchanted with the health care system, including:

- The quality of medical care they can provide

- Their inability to practice preventive medicine

- Their limited ability to direct their careers

- Their prospects for financial security

With the growth in medical bureaucracies, the question becomes *"Is the patient lost along with the caring physician?"* If you were to ask physicians and patients this question, the answer you would most often get is a resounding yes.

Concierge medicine allows primary care physicians to regain control over their practice of medicine by enabling them to put the patient front and center. It also lets them regain control over their careers and their ability to succeed. Concierge medicine provides physicians medical autonomy with the right to make unimpeded health care decisions based on their expertise and their knowledge of individual patient needs.

For patients, the most important benefit of concierge medicine is that it provides a much higher level of personalized attention and medical care than you would otherwise be able to attain. Consequently, it creates a strong sense of security, control and long-term trust.

Categories of conditions

To better understand concierge medicine, consider three categories of health conditions physicians deal with:

1. Acute problems

2. Chronic conditions

3. Longevity care

Let's look at each category.

Acute problems are short-term, often-severe medical issues that dramatically affect the patient's quality of life. An example is food poisoning, with its classic symptoms of nausea, vomiting, fever and a complete lack of energy. If physicians can diagnose and treat it early, then they can dramatically shorten the length of the acute event.

Another example is a heart attack. Again, time to treatment is most important, in this case for survival. A physician who recognizes the seriousness of the situation and begins treatment will dramatically increase the chances of the patient's survival.

Another variant of acute problems is time-limited conditions. These are health issues that come with an "expiration date," either because of time or environment. Pregnancy is an obvious example, but location-specific conditions can be severe. For example, if malaria is present in a tropical country where a patient is traveling, that risk must be managed until the patient leaves the area.

In a more specific example, the patriarch of a well-known family consistently experienced painful arthritis within days of relocating to his winter residence. The arthritis would invariably resolve when he left this home. A careful interview by his concierge physician diagnosed the problem: At his winter home, the patient was inclined to eat fish and shellfish (dishes that he loved) two or three times per day. The sudden large uptick in his protein intake was provoking his arthritis, which was similar to but not as severe as gout.

Chronic conditions are issues that endure and require long-term medications and therapies. Hypertension and diabetes are common examples.

Both of these conditions require regular collection of a key data point (i.e., blood pressure and blood sugar, respectively) that reflects how well the condition is being managed.

With formally calendared care and active ongoing close management, the impact of these chronic conditions can be quite minimal. Without proper ongoing management, their impact can become serious, or even lethal, over time. Unmanaged diabetes can go on to erode vision, kidney function and heart function, eventually leading to organ failure and death. Likewise, untreated or unmanaged hypertension can create an extremely high risk for a debilitating stroke or heart attack.

Longevity care is a relatively new medical care model. It's an aggressive form of preventive medicine built around managing personal health risks by identifying pre-existing genetic risk factors and key biomarkers, and then addressing them through a holistic, lifelong protocol. When risk is identified and managed early, potential negative outcomes can be delayed, lessened and even completely prevented. It's not about treating an existing condition but rather taking highly accurate and focused preventive actions to avoid possible problems in the future.

As we will see in upcoming chapters, high-quality concierge medical practices are generally more capable of addressing these conditions than is the traditional health care system. Drawing their roots from true primary care and active prevention, modern concierge medical practices are built to address these categories of conditions to the benefit of the health and life span of their patients.

Key elements of concierge medicine

The core defining characteristic of concierge medicine is that there is a retainer arrangement—a "membership fee"—for access to the physician or the service. While much of concierge medicine is physician-driven, there is a version of concierge care known as "private health advisory" or "professional health advocacy" that is not. We'll discuss the different versions of concierge medicine in Chapter 5.

The retainer fee is principally for the personal time and professional expertise of the primary care physician and the additional personal logistical support provided by his or her office staff.

For many people, the powerful appeal of most concierge medical practices is on-demand physician access. This might be by phone or in person, or increasingly by way of the Internet. Traditional primary care physicians may have thousands of patients, coupled with financial pressures, so their offices often have long appointment delays and the plague of seven-minute medicine. In contrast, concierge physicians are motivated to make themselves available and spend the time they need to ensure their patients are truly cared for.

Just about all versions of concierge medical practices act as health care advocates and facilitators. They help patients source the specialists they need and coordinate care, as well as follow up with the patient and the specialists. Health care advocates also help patients understand exactly what is happening in their care and assist them in making informed decisions. Given the importance of health care advocates, let's take a closer look at the role.

Concierge physician as health care advocate

In most every situation, the best form of health care advocate is a physician—not a nurse or a nurse practitioner or a professional "navigator." There are many reasons for this, including the fact that physicians tend to return calls of other physicians much more rapidly. As the number of "private health advisory" companies has grown, many physicians and surgeons have learned to ignore the calls of nurses and "navigators" because they are increasingly flooded with them and do not welcome the inquiries of "navigators" with minimal clinical training.

Having said this, patients can meaningfully benefit from these types of health care advocates if they have any sort of complex or difficult-to-diagnose condition. Complex cases become more common with age, especially when chronic conditions like obesity or hypertension become part of the patient's overall personal health, and so a higher level of expertise in the form of a qualified second opinion from the advocate can be helpful.

CASE EXAMPLE

The primary care physician of a patient with shoulder pain referred him to an orthopedist who could not see him for five weeks, which meant five more weeks of shoulder pain and the loss of the patient's golf game. In response to this delay, the patient joined a concierge medical practice. To address the patient's relentless shoulder pain, the concierge physician contacted a competent orthopedist he knew personally and summarized the patient's prior clinical course, closing with a request that the orthopedist see the patient sooner rather than later.

The orthopedist, keen to maintain his referral relationship with the concierge physician, instructed his staff to put the patient at the top of the office appointment cancellation list. In the interim, the concierge practice arranged for this new member to have a shoulder MRI, as recommended by the orthopedist, in advance of his office visit. The patient was seen within one week. In this case, the concierge physician was both a major health care advocate and a time saver for the patient.

CASE EXAMPLE

A patient was diagnosed at a local community hospital with an unusual form of breast cancer. The best care for this form of cancer was available at only seven hospitals in the entire U.S. To get the patient to one of these experts, the concierge physician's office collected all the lab results, images and other physician records of her case. Summarizing them in a single information packet, the physician's office contacted specific physician specialists at five of the seven hospitals, transferred the consolidated records to three of them and secured an appointment for the patient within two weeks at two of them.

The concierge physician and staff acted as strong health care advocates in arranging for the patient to go to the selected hospital and ensuring all her records were properly transferred. In this case, addressing the complexity of her cancer while enabling a rapid and holistic transfer of clinical information made the process far easier for the patient.

Being able to navigate the complexity of the health care system and "fight" for their patients is a characteristic of high-quality concierge medical practices. It has become a very important responsibility and, in some cases, can be the difference between life and death.

Who becomes a concierge medical physician?

Not every type of physician is appropriate to deliver concierge medicine, so it's important to understand the types of physicians and their qualities. Likewise, only certain types of medical practices lend themselves to becoming concierge medical practices. Three specialties are particularly well-suited:

1. Internal medicine: general expertise in the diseases of aging and adult medicine

2. Emergency care: broadest range of diagnostic experience with all ages

3. Family medicine: all ages, with an emphasis on holistic health

Rarely, a high-functioning concierge medical practice will integrate physicians from all three of these specialties. Less common, though increasingly more prevalent, are specialist concierge medical practices. These tend to be centered on endocrinology (diabetes) and cardiology (pre-existing heart disease).

In any scenario where the physician has an ongoing long-term relationship with the patient, there is an opportunity to establish a concierge medical practice. Clearly, where the physician has short-duration, single-event patient involvement, such as in the case of an orthopedic surgery or a radiologist's interpretation of an X-ray, a concierge medical practice is not an option. At its most basic, the definition of a concierge physician is this: He or she is the first physician you turn to when you have a health problem.

Food for thought

Armed with the information you've gained so far, you're ready to answer this important question:

Should you and your family become patients of a concierge medical practice?

You are interested in the concept, as evidenced by your reading this book. We know from qualitative and quantitative research as well as our own experiences that people take a number of factors into account when making this decision. These are some of the most important ones:

- Your concern for your personal health care and that of your loved ones

- Your level of confidence in the traditional health care system

- Your understanding of the different types of concierge medical practices

- Your finances

Though we are posing the question now, you probably need more information to make a sound decision. So we'll look next at exactly how concierge medicine differs from the traditional health care system you already know.

CHAPTER 4

How Concierge Medicine Is Different

In comparing concierge medical practices to traditional medical practices, there are a few decisive differences that most people would say show the superiority of the concierge medical model. However, it's important to realize that some concierge medical services can be delivered by traditional medical practices. Some of these services will increasingly become available from more medical practices. Even so, the primary issues are still quality and time.

Services of concierge medical practices

There are a number of services that typically distinguish concierge medicine from the traditional health care delivery system. However, not every concierge medical practice provides every potential service. The following are the core services of many types of concierge medical practices.

At 3:00 p.m., the voice coach of a headline performer called from San Francisco to ask for advice. Her young pupil was congested and missing key notes. Interviewed by phone, the performer was clearly hoarse. Using her personal prescription medical kit under the direction of her concierge medical practice physician, the singer was immediately treated with both prednisone and albuterol mist breathing treatments. A senior ear, nose and throat specialist from a leading medical university was called in to do a house call. His exam affirmed the treatment, and the curtain went up on time. The headliner's voice was right on key.

24/7, immediate on-call physicians

Getting access to a physician whenever medical services are required is the cornerstone of many higher-end concierge medical practices. Quick access to a high-caliber physician for timely diagnosis and immediate treatment saves lives and prevents acute problems from becoming critical.

CASE EXAMPLE

If an outbreak of ocular shingles is not treated quickly with topical and systemic antivirals, it can be an ocular disaster. Without a timely and correct diagnosis, a patient with ocular shingles could easily lose vision in that eye. After a grueling 17-hour flight to Tokyo, a patient experienced the rapid onset of pain and redness in her right eye. With the pain increasing, the patient called her concierge doctor in New York, who correctly diagnosed her with an acute outbreak of ocular shingles. The physician directed treatment with the exact medication needed and coordinated a next-day appointment with an ophthalmologist in Singapore, the next destination on the patient's business trip. The ophthalmologist confirmed the diagnosis, advised the patient to continue treatment and then provided a set of notes for her concierge doctor to give the ophthalmologist at the patient's home hospital in the U.S. She completed her treatment and suffered no permanent visual impairment.

CASE EXAMPLE

A 3-year-old was suddenly unable to use his right arm. No visible bruising or deformity was seen during a guided FaceTime exam. The child was diagnosed with a "nursemaid's elbow," or a dislocated radial head—a commonly seen dislocation that occurs when a toddler is lifted by the arm. After reviewing a YouTube video on the procedure, the father, under real-time video link guidance, performed the maneuver to fix the dislocation within five minutes. The child began using his arm normally and the entire family was spared a trip to the emergency room.

The "golden hour" refers to the length of time from the onset of a major life-threatening event, such as a heart attack or stroke, to the time the person receives medical treatment and severe damage is avoided. Speed to diagnosis and speed to treatment determine the patient outcome.

For instance, physicians use the expression "Time is muscle" to describe the fixed amount of time to intervene in the event of a heart attack. There are very clear time windows that determine survival in the case of a heart attack:

- The patient's heart becomes electrically unstable within the first five to 30 minutes of the attack.

- If the heart muscle goes without oxygen for three hours, it dies permanently.

- If treatment is initiated rapidly with aspirin, nitroglycerin and a beta-blocker (to slow the heart rate), the patient gains more time until the definitive procedure of a cardiac angioplasty (the surgical repair of the blocked blood vessel) and recovery can begin.

Another example where the golden hour comes into play is when a child with a severe allergy is exposed to his or her allergen. For patients in these situations, the ability to receive an accurate diagnosis and quick medical care is critical, making 24/7, immediate on-call physicians potentially essential.

Second opinion availability

Medicine is both a science and an art. Good health care is also about having access to vetted and recognized field leader specialists for serious and complex diseases, such as cancer and Parkinsonism. The ability to get high-quality second opinions for verification of a diagnosis or for different perspectives on treatment is often a crucial resource provided by concierge medical practices.

In all of medicine, there are subtypes and variants of all common diseases, as well as nearly "orphan" diseases that call for a second opinion. If you have a complex, rare form of a disease, you are best cared for in a hospital that serves as a magnet for your particular rare and complex disease.

Moreover, there are physicians who have devoted their entire careers to single diseases such as Parkinsonism, Crohn's disease and unusual diseases of aging like hemochromatosis (excess iron in the blood) and polycythemia (a type of bone marrow disorder). When seeking care, you want the physician who is the expert and leader, not the physician who happens to be on staff at your medical center. Once you identify the expert, you need a physician-to-physician referral to assist in getting an appointment; otherwise you risk waiting for months.

CASE EXAMPLE

A patient who appeared to have an unusual autoimmune joint disease was referred to a local rheumatologist by his concierge physician. The rheumatologist did a thorough, standard collection of tests that did not yield a diagnosis. At that point, the patient asked for a second opinion. All his records were collected, summarized and quickly transferred to a leading medical center near Washington, D.C. An appointment was made through a doctor-to-doctor referral. Two trips, a battery of blood tests and a joint MRI later, his diagnosis was confirmed: stage II Lyme disease, originally acquired on a vacation to Nantucket two years prior.

Complete case continuity

Having a qualified physician overseeing treatment across specialists can be both efficient and effective. It ensures higher quality of care and decreases the possibility of errors. It ties into the importance of a centralized, consolidated medical record. For example, in the event of a heart attack, critical images and information, like a baseline EKG or prior cardiac catheterization report, can be lifesaving. When a prior baseline EKG is immediately accessible, it can quickly be compared to the new ER EKG, making any harmful change immediately apparent. Typically, if there's no change, a physician can quickly avoid an intensive, painful procedure like a cardiac catheterization.

CASE EXAMPLE

A patient traveling between homes in three different regions has atrial fibrillation (irregular heart rhythm) as a result of aging. Her heart rate and blood viscosity must be frequently measured to prevent complications. Additionally, she must take a blood thinner and be tested regularly to ensure that this medication is effective wherever she is.

In this patient's case, continuity of medical information is critical, as is the scheduling of supporting blood tests and the collection of data from a smartphone-connected cardiac rhythm monitor. All this information, from the most recent lab values to today's heart rhythm, needs to be centralized and easily accessible. Most important, this information needs to be summarized into a single document for rapid referral in an emergency.

Secure 24/7 access to medical records

Especially in times of emergency, being able to immediately obtain your medical information can be crucial. It is also essential that patient medical records be secure and generally inaccessible except by designated physicians and in the event of a health care emergency.

CASE EXAMPLE

An LA-based hedge fund manager with a known history of epilepsy takes the overnight red-eye flight to New York for a key meeting. In his rush to get to LAX, he forgets to take his daily seizure medication. Arriving sleep-deprived and under-medicated, he has a seizure at JFK. When EMS arrives, they assume this is a new seizure. They transport him to the local hospital, which has been alerted and is preparing the CT scanner, the on-call neurologist and the critical care team in response.

While the manager is en route to the hospital, his co-worker called his concierge physician's answering service and received a call back two minutes later. The on-call doctor called the emergency room, explained the situation and faxed a copy of the manager's summarized medical records.

Instead of undertaking an uninformed and painful (for the patient) search for the cause of the seizure, the emergency room staff checked his medication levels (which were low) and gave him a rapid IV dose to restore a therapeutic level of medication. The patient was discharged three hours later and went to his department meeting that night. Based on the speed of accessing and transferring his medical information, the manager was saved a potential hospital admission. Additionally, he was spared long bouts of blood testing, a claustrophobia-inducing CT scan and possibly a second seizure in the emergency room.

Confidentiality of patient information should be paramount in any medical practice. At one high-end concierge medical practice, patients can get their medical records at any time of day, but they must talk directly to a member of the support staff as part of a two-step authentication process for identity verification. The staff member checks the identity of the caller, who must correctly answer a secret question while also using the thumbprint feature on their iPhone. This approach of a human-to-human, real-time interaction coupled with two-step authentication is not possible within most medical centers. It is no coincidence that hospitals have been targets of hacking.

Longevity planning

It's now possible to lengthen your life span, thanks to advances in genomics and the use of a formal longevity protocol. And not only can you live longer, but you also can maintain a very high quality of life. Not surprisingly, there is considerable demand for such expertise.

The intense interest in being able to live a long and healthy life makes certain concierge medical practices very attractive. We address this topic in detail in Chapter 6.

Access to leading specialists and medical centers

When specialists need to be consulted, the ability to connect with leading authorities and the medical centers where they work can be lifesaving. Having knowledge of and access to these experts—wherever they are in the country or in the world—is an important component of many concierge medical practices.

A potentially major problem is that many physicians are contractually bound to refer only to specialists in their medical center or network. This may not always be the best option for a patient. Like in every profession, there is a broad range in specialist quality. In general, the best field-specific specialists are found in densely populated areas, where they deal with just one condition that they regularly see.

CASE EXAMPLE

At a leading hospital, a patient was told that the only solution to his herniated lumbar disc and painful chronic sciatica was a spinal fusion. In this serious procedure, two vertebrae are bolted together, so the patient's range of motion at that level is lost, which leads to an eventual deterioration of the lumbar discs above and below the fusion point. Spinal fusion was the standard of care ten years ago. Now the standard of care is an artificial disc replacement (ADR) using a prosthetic disc insert.

Armed with the knowledge that a better ADR prosthetic device was available in Europe, the patient's concierge physician's office organized the key MRIs and exam data for forwarding to a world-class spine surgeon in Germany. This surgeon had performed more than 2,000 procedures with the improved spinal disc prosthesis. He concluded that the patient was a good candidate for the procedure. Postoperatively, the patient did well and had a full recovery of range of motion and, most important, experienced no more chronic pain.

Access to the best specialists and medical centers is especially important if the patient is a candidate for an emerging therapy. This is a particular issue in surgery, because most surgeons do not continually learn new procedures after they leave their residencies.

Connected monitoring

With the adoption of smartphones and similar technologies, the ability to monitor a patient's health from a distance is becoming more common. This monitoring delivers a lot more data upon which to base better treatment decisions, thus creating better outcomes for the patient affected by a chronic illness.

Connected monitoring is rapidly emerging as the best way to manage a chronic condition. Currently, the most common chronic conditions for monitoring are hypertension, diabetes, atrial fibrillation and asthma. For one of these conditions, the patient carries a small personal monitor that is connected through Bluetooth to a smartphone. Every time the patient uses the monitor, a data point is generated that gets sent to a database, where it joins the patient's data file.

If there's an abnormal reading, rules that are written into the database flag it for immediate intervention. As long as there's a monitor that generates a relevant data point, the day-to-day management of the condition no longer depends on a physician office visit.

For example, instead of getting a blood pressure reading once a month, you could measure your own blood pressure three times per day, every day. Instead of a data set of four office-based blood pressure readings taken over two to three months, there could be 100 over the same time frame. This larger data set gives a much more accurate picture of how your blood pressure is being managed.

This model of connected monitoring is becoming the gold standard, rendering incredible efficiency and success in the management of chronic conditions. Both patients and their doctors are benefiting from its ease and accuracy.

Another powerful benefit of connected monitoring is its ability to identify a patient who may be at risk for a near-term health event. For children with asthma, a peak flow meter (which measures lung elasticity and breathing ability) is used to provide an accurate picture of how well their asthma is being managed. If a peak flow meter suddenly records a low peak flow rate, immediate intervention is required. If the number is critically low, the emergency medical service is notified and treatment starts at home while waiting for the ambulance.

Among the 80 million Americans with hypertension who would benefit from this model, algorithm-based rules can identify a single data point as dangerous (for example, a blood pressure reading of 220/120) or identify a worrisome trend over time (for example, blood pressure gradually increasing to an average of 150/95 over a month). Such early warnings can ensure effective treatment, prevent complications and save lives.

Tele-diagnosis and treatment

The ability to use mobile technology to evaluate and treat patients is often critical for 24/7, immediate on-call physicians. As the technology evolves, the range and quality of diagnosis and treatment will as well. The key to success in this endeavor is having the right tools for both doctors *and* their distant patients.

At its simplest, the ability to capture a medical history and do a simple, remote-guided exam via voice or video enables doctors to provide medical care outside their offices. This new capability is unique and truly revolutionary. There are myriad benefits:

- **Convenience.** An app is put on patients' phones that allows them to contact their concierge physician's office and to speak with their concierge physician immediately via phone or video.

- **Speed.** With this rapid physician access, lifesaving interventions can be made immediately, and the patient does not have to wait or suffer a delay that results in unnecessary pain and suffering. Because a physician is doing the evaluation, a subsequent specialist referral can also happen quickly and accurately since it's occurring on a physician-to-physician level.

- **Follow-up.** Because medicine is being practiced in a technologically connected environment, follow-up is increasingly easy and assured. When a case is addressed, the concierge physician and the care team already know how to reach the patient, so follow-up is calendared, executed and guaranteed. This is important because if there has been a misdiagnosis or a change in symptoms, the connection to the patient ensures that the issue gets detected much earlier. All of this enables the best outcome.

Destination medical planning

For people who travel, knowing that reliable medical resources are locally available in different locations is extremely reassuring. Foreknowledge of nearby medical resources can be lifesaving in the case of a medical crisis like a heart attack or major trauma. This becomes even more important when people are traveling internationally—especially in foreign lands where the level of medical care might not be comparable to a developed country's.

There are also unique local medical risks. Medical geo-surveillance is often a critical component of destination medical planning. Specifically, a great many of the infectious diseases in the world change seasonally because they are related to factors like elevation, rainfall and the corresponding mosquito population. Because of this, not being aware of local changes can present a major risk to your personal health.

In many cases, this kind of information is available, but it must be researched on a frequent basis. For instance, you should know if there has been a recent outbreak of cholera in a particular country you are visiting if that country is about to enter the rainy season.

CASE EXAMPLE

While on a trip with her family, a child came down with dengue fever in a rural area of Cambodia. Dengue fever is a very painful mosquito-borne disease. Thanks to a pre-trip medical due diligence report on the area, the family's concierge physicians were already aware of a modern medical clinic that could treat this kind of serious case. That knowledge—acquired in advance of the need—made a rapid effective response possible and the patient experienced no delay in diagnosis and treatment.

Foreign physician/hospital database

In relation to destination medical planning, it's important to recognize that the competence of local physicians varies widely around the world. This is especially apparent in China, for example, where conventional Western-style credentialing is not prevalent. Foreknowledge of credentialed and licensed providers is critical. This becomes particularly important if you are visiting multiple destinations over a brief period of time, as an illness may start in one city and continue as you complete your travel itinerary.

This makes having a vetted list of qualified local physicians and medical centers with the appropriate professional qualifications and record of clinical competence a key asset to staying healthy during travel.

CASE EXAMPLE

A patient contracted bronchitis while on a trip to Japan. As the patient traveled to Beijing, the bronchitis became much worse, and he was started on antibiotics from his personal medical kit. By the night he arrived in Beijing, he had a fever and his kit's portable pulse oximeter (which measures the oxygen saturation level in blood) showed that his saturation level had dropped by a few percentage points, from 98 percent (normal) to 94 percent (low).

While the patient was in Beijing, his concierge physician used his global credentialed personal provider database to identify the best facility to have a chest X-ray done. His concierge physician forwarded the results to the physicians at his next destination, Singapore. In addition, a U.S.-based radiologist received the same files and confirmed that this patient had pneumonia. Despite being on antibiotics, the patient did not substantially improve. In response to this lack of progress, a decision was made to hospitalize the patient for two days at a modern local hospital. Post-discharge, he safely returned home and made a full recovery.

Global medical evacuation

It is very appealing for people who travel abroad to have a fully funded evacuation plan to bring them home if they are hospitalized overseas.

Historically, evacuation insurance has been bundled into travel assistance programs that include everything from eyeglass repair to physician-finding services. For the most part, they are evacuation plans structured as insurance policies.

When a policy is activated, a medical representative of the insurance company makes a clinical decision about whether the patient needs to be evacuated. This creates a built-in conflict of interest. In many cases, the insurer has a financial incentive to limit air evacuation and instead transport patients to the nearest hospital that is acceptable in their opinion. This is unacceptable for families that have come to expect excellent personal support and quality resources.

Instead, it's critical that the medical evacuation plan bring the patient all the way back to his or her home or designated hospital, not "to the nearest, most appropriate medical center." Not surprisingly, a premium medical evacuation policy like this is strongly correlated with rapid access to leading specialists at major medical centers, as well as detailed destination medical planning.

Personal medical resources

Starting effective treatment immediately with a medication from a personalized medical resource, like a prescription medical kit, saves time and dramatically improves the outcome in a crisis, like chest pain or an overwhelming allergic reaction—both of which can occur anytime without warning.

CASE EXAMPLE

For an NYC-based patient who has sustained a broken femur in a car accident in Moscow, the quality of his travel assistance policy is key to the quality of his health care experience. With a typical travel assistance policy, he may or may not be flown to Helsinki (the best nearest hospital) and most certainly will not be evacuated all the way back to the U.S.

The gold standard for medical evacuation is a policy that flies the patient all the way to his or her home hospital or to a designated specialist hospital of choice, if indicated. For the case of the patient with a fractured femur, the ideal course of action was immediate evacuation to his home hospital in Manhattan. If the fracture was deemed severe, the evacuation policy should take him all the way to the best hospital available for orthopedic femur reconstruction.

As we'll discuss in the next chapter, access to personalized medical resources can come in several forms depending on the nature of the concierge medical practice. These resources can range from a personally dedicated physician who travels with the clients to a 24/7, on-call physician team to a personal prescription medical kit for guided use by a concierge doctor when needed. Exhibit 4.1 shows a picture of the two types of personal prescription medical kits provided by WorldClinic to its patients. The suitcase version is for homes, yachts and even private jets. The smaller, hand-held version is for personal use, especially when traveling.

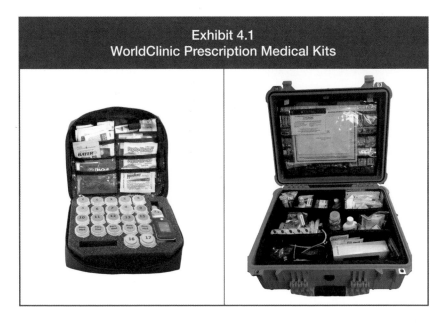

Exhibit 4.1
WorldClinic Prescription Medical Kits

Having customized medical supply kits is appealing, but such kits by themselves often have very limited value. However, when they are part of a delivery model where physicians are guiding their use, as in the case of telemedicine, they can be an invaluable asset for immediately treating an emerging crisis or preventing a small problem from becoming a big one.

Along with their ability to speed treatment, personal prescription medical kits have several other important characteristics:

- Many people assume that drugs in other parts of the world are effective and accurately labeled. This is false. In other parts of the world, particularly developing countries, there is a significant chance that medications are placebo, out-of-date or inaccurately labeled. Having a set of high-quality U.S.-made pharmaceuticals is insurance against this risk.

- When a knowledgeable physician designs the kits, they are highly effective in providing powerful treatment. For example, a good personal prescription medical kit often comes with 14 to 17 prescription medications. These should be labeled specifically to the patient, with appropriate direction and dosage information, from a licensed pharmacy.

- There should be a full accompanying set of documents signed by the physician attesting to the origin and contents of the kit to prevent misunderstandings with customs and border security agents.

Food for thought

One of the greatest obstacles to good health care has been the explosion of disorganized and unfiltered medical information on new medical advances. Many of these innovations are truly valuable, even lifesaving, but they are not integrated into today's clinical practices primarily because they are not attached to a third-party billing code.

In many cases, these innovations are available to the public, but because they are not covered by insurance, they are not well-known. This is a major missed opportunity on the path to great personal health. A truly great concierge practice has a formal mechanism for staying fully informed of the latest innovations and how to access them both in the U.S. and abroad. We discuss the application of this cutting-edge care further in Chapter 9, where we outline trends in concierge medical care, and in Chapter 10, where we provide a framework for selecting a concierge practice.

In this chapter, we discussed the services and capabilities of many concierge medical practices. As we'll see in the next chapter, there are many variations of concierge medicine practices providing some or all of these services to different degrees—and sometimes none at all.

You should think about these questions:

Which of these myriad services are important to you?

Which of these services do you consider essential?

Which are "nice to have" but not critical?

So far, we've been talking about concierge medicine as a single service. However, there are several variations in the way concierge medicine is delivered that you should know about. We turn next to the different types of concierge medical practices and the services each one provides.

CHAPTER 5

Variations on a Theme

As we've seen, concierge medicine is a unique type of primary health care delivery. In contrast to conventional medicine, its care model is customized to meet the needs of each individual patient. One size does not fit all when it comes to patients' wants, preferences and budgets. Today, the annual cost of a concierge membership ranges from hundreds of dollars to more than $1 million per year. This considerable range in cost means there are considerable differences between the various types of concierge medical practices.

In this chapter, we're going to break down the different types of concierge medical practices with respect to the services we discussed in the previous chapter. Keep in mind that we're looking at broad categories and that there is a great deal of variation within each category.

A 46-year-old business owner felt a burning pain in his lower back the night before a critical industry speech. Convinced he had a kidney stone, he called the physician hotline of his concierge medical practice. A four-minute interview and guided exam revealed the diagnosis: an acute outbreak of lumbar shingles. He was immediately treated with medication from his personal prescription medical kit.

His care team tracked his progress, and his case resolved three weeks later. As a result of the immediate diagnosis and treatment, there was zero downtime for this busy executive.

Different types of concierge medical practices

Concierge medicine is driven by patients' desires for loyalty, efficiency and competence, along with access to top-of-the-line physicians and state-of-the-art diagnosis and treatment. Different types of practices meet these patient desires in different ways. While concierge medicine is regularly talked about as a single service, in reality there are many variations.

Exhibit 5.1 provides an overview of the main categories of concierge medical practices in terms of the services they deliver. For the sake of comparison, it also includes the conventional physician practice you are very likely already familiar with through your own experience.

While there are currently many clear distinctions among the types of offerings, it's likely that some differences will blur over time. For example, as mobile technology improves and concierge medicine matures, some costs will come down, and telemedical options for chronic disease monitoring will multiply and may become the norm in all medical practices.

Physician concierge practices

There are three types of physician concierge practices, and many versions of each (see Exhibit 5.2). These are the three types:

1. **Independent concierge medical practices.** These practices may or may not accept insurance but do charge fixed, annual retainers for which they provide services in addition to conventional medical care. They provide a higher-level patient experience by ensuring greater access through rapid callbacks, extended office hours and

Exhibit 5.1 Variations on a Theme				
Deliverables	Physician Concierge Practice	Private Health Advisory	Continuous Connected Care Practice	Conventional Physician Practice
Physician directed	Yes	No	Yes	Yes
24/7, immediate on-call physicians	Varies	Not applicable	Yes	Usually callback
Second opinion	Yes	Yes	Yes	Yes
Complete case continuity	Yes	Potentially	Yes	Rarely
Secure 24/7 access to medical records	Yes	Yes	Yes	Possibly
Longevity planning	Yes	Yes	Yes	Possibly
Access to leading specialists and medical centers	Regularly	Yes	Yes	Possibly
Connected monitoring	Varies	Not applicable	Yes	Rarely
Tele-diagnosis and treatment	Regularly	Not applicable	Yes	Rarely
Destination medical planning	Varies	Yes	Yes	No
Foreign physician/ hospital database	Varies	Sometimes	Yes	No
Global medical evacuation	Varies	Yes	Yes	No
Personal medical resources	Varies	Not applicable	Yes	No

shorter wait times. A variation of this type of concierge physician also exists inside a larger hospital system, often in the form of an "executive," "premier" or "signature" health care office.

2. **Networked concierge physician practices.** The archetype of this kind of concierge practice is nationwide company MDVIP. The physicians of MDVIP may be independent and community-based, or affiliated with a larger medical center. In all cases, physicians split the annual patient membership fees with MDVIP, which does the marketing and business management consulting for their practices to maximize their chances of success.

3. **Exclusive physician concierge medical practices.** This is the most elite form of concierge medicine. It exists when a very wealthy individual or family has its very own exclusive, high-caliber physician or even a team of excellent physicians on retainer. Central to this arrangement is that the physicians are exclusive to the person or family, as they have no other patients. These physicians tend to be quite experienced and exceptional in their diagnostic acumen and interpersonal skills.

Private health advisories

These are commercial firms to which patients pay a fixed fee to purchase a certain set of non-physician services, typically including:

- A relationship with a "navigator," who may or may not have a formal medical background, to facilitate appointments and collect information.

	Exhibit 5.2 Types of Physician Concierge Practices		
Deliverables	**Independent Physician**	**Networked Physician**	**Exclusive Physician**
24/7, immediate on-call physicians	Potentially	Regularly	Yes
Second opinion	Yes	Yes	Yes
Complete case continuity	Yes	Yes	Yes
Secure 24/7 access to medical records	Regularly	Yes	Yes
Longevity planning	Yes	Yes	Yes
Access to leading specialists and medical centers	Rarely	Regularly	Yes
Connected monitoring	Increasingly yes	Increasingly yes	Yes
Tele-diagnosis and treatment	Increasingly yes	Increasingly yes	Yes
Destination medical planning	Sometimes	Sometimes	Yes
Foreign physician/ hospital database	Rarely	Sometimes	Yes
Global medical evacuation	Rarely	Sometimes	Yes
Personal medical resources	Rarely	Sometimes	Yes— administered by physician on-site

- For complex cases, a review of clinical information by an advisory group of physicians affiliated with the firm. This group will then render an opinion as to where the patient should go for a higher level of care.

- Third-party travel assistance and executive physical exam scheduling.

It's important to recognize that private health advisory firms do not practice medicine and therefore—from a physician's perspective—do not take fundamental responsibility for the patient's outcome. In a private health advisory firm, there is no bona fide physician-patient relationship. In addition, advisories are not a solution for acute medical problems, since the care model necessitates referrals to physicians for care.

Continuous connected care practices

These types of medical practices use the connectivity provided by technology to deliver care and ensure continuity in the patient experience, regardless of their location or time of day.

These practices' connectivity allows them to provide patients with a personal virtual "emergency room" by integrating an on-call physician and care team with personal prescription medical kits and a comprehensive, global, credentialed provider network. This enables an ill or injured patient to usually access care amazingly quickly, be diagnosed quickly and be treated immediately with the contents of the personal prescription medical kits. This type of care is both convenient and efficient. From experience, we know that more than nine out of ten cases can be resolved through smartphone access to a physician and the prescription medical kit.

More serious cases are quickly referred to a higher level of care with complete informational continuity and ongoing case tracking. Using a smartphone, the practice can capture a patient's location and map it against a pre-credentialed database of high-quality hospitals and physicians. This translates into immediately knowing the fastest route to the most appropriate higher level of local care. This eliminates delays in searching for a hospital or going to the wrong hospital in a time-sensitive crisis.

The connected concierge medical practice's use of technology also makes it much easier to monitor simple chronic diseases like hypertension, atrial fibrillation and diabetes. The simple monitors for these diseases can be paired with a smartphone and daily data points sent to a command center for interpretation and action as needed.

Connected concierge practices are also taking advantage of digital informatics. The connected concierge medical practice is more digitally aware. As such, it's well-positioned to both track and know the patient's health in extreme detail, as well as take advantage of every new data-driven innovation related to genome, biomarkers, personal monitors, and any other predictive or tracking tool for the patient.

The connectivity of this care model means that all of the patient's data can be turned into actionable steps for both patient and physician. This is an important advantage because right now there is no mechanism to turn individual data into health improvements; the average EMR system does not share patient information easily, so the patient is left with an extraordinarily complex database that holds their health information and future predictive risk but no way to act on that information.

In the near future, digital connectivity and fully integrated predictive risk markers like a person's genome will be coupled with best practices prevention protocol to create an actionable, personalized lifetime health plan that could enable patients to live dramatically longer life spans.

The important point in all of this is that continuously connected care concierge medical practices are at the forefront of leveraging technology to provide diagnosis and treatment, making personal health care easier and faster. At the same time, they are laying the groundwork for a lifetime, genome-based personal plan for maximizing longevity.

Not wanting to be left behind, the conventional concierge medical practice community is adopting some of the innovations validated by continuously connected concierge care practices. This trend will continue and no doubt represents the future.

Dealing with different categories of conditions

A good way to understand and compare the different types of concierge medical practices is to look at how they address the three types of commonly seen health conditions (see **Exhibit 5.3**). Remember that there are wide variations within each type of practice, so these are broad generalizations. We have again included the conventional physician practice for comparison's sake.

	Exhibit 5.3 Dealing with Different Categories of Conditions			
Category	Physician Concierge Practice	Private Health Advisory	Continuous Connected Care Practice	Conventional Physician Practice
Acute conditions	In most circumstances	No	Yes	During office hours
Chronic conditions	Yes, usually office-based only	Often as a coordinator	Yes, connected monitors to track and manage	Yes, office-based only
Longevity care	Sometimes	No	Yes	No

Continuous connected care and physician concierge practices are designed to deal with acute conditions. Keep in mind that physicians are driving these practices. Meanwhile, private health advisories are geared toward helping patients deal with unique conditions, many of them complex or severe. They do this by taking on a coordinator role, arranging for specialists.

In contrast, continuous connected care and physician concierge medical practices often address chronic conditions in their roles as both clinical physicians and personal health care advocates.

As for formal longevity planning and management, the continuous connected care concierge practice is most likely to provide this expertise, though we predict that physician concierge practices will follow suit in the years to come.

Because physician concierge practices can encompass the greatest range of medical practice, it's useful to look at how the three principal types deal with the different categories of conditions (see Exhibit 5.4).

	Exhibit 5.4 Physician Concierge Practices and Categories of Conditions		
Category	**Independent Physician**	**Networked Physician**	**Exclusive Physician**
Acute conditions	In most circumstances	Yes	Yes
Chronic conditions	As a health care advocate	As a health care advocate	Directly or as a health care advocate
Longevity care	Rarely	Sometimes	Yes

The independent concierge physician can address most acute conditions in a timely manner. When it comes to chronic conditions, many of these physicians act as health care advocates. Today, they rarely provide longevity care, though they are expected to do so in the future.

Concierge medical practices based within hospital systems are very capable of dealing with acute conditions. For chronic conditions, the physician acts as the patient's health care advocate within the system. Some of them are involved in delivering various versions of longevity care, something that is more often a decision of the hospital's care review board.

Exclusive physician concierge medical practices deal with all three categories. If you can afford to have a continuously available world-class physician or, better yet, a team of world-class physicians who are connected to the top medical facilities and have the appropriate support staff, then you're likely to have the finest possible medical care.

Food for thought

In general, the best type of concierge medical practice is the exclusive physician version, where the physician is unquestionably world-class. While we will provide some examples of this version later, it's far—very far—from common. Why? It's likely to be the most expensive version of concierge medicine and can easily cost a person or family millions of dollars a year. But it's regularly the best. After all, there's typically one highly competent doctor (and sometimes more) for just one family.

Taking the exclusive concierge physician off the table, the other versions run from a couple of thousand dollars to tens of thousands of dollars a year. Given that, consider these questions:

Which version of concierge medicine do you find most appealing?

What about that version do you think is essential and what is simply nice to have?

When it comes to concierge medical practices, you have options. By understanding the different services available and deciding what is essential and what is nice to have, you become a more astute consumer.

As we have looked across this industry, a service that is proving to be extremely important to more and more people is longevity planning. It is being woven into an increasing number of concierge medical practices and is probably going to be the cornerstone of a number of them in the next few years. We discuss this trend in the next chapter.

CHAPTER 6

Do You Want to Live to 120 or Beyond?

We are at the beginning of a medical revolution where it will be possible to seriously extend the lives of people, even curing them of diseases that are fatal today. These individuals will not only be able to live longer, but they will also have fuller, well-lived lives—lives characterized by enduring physical mobility and mental sharpness. The key to this longevity is twofold: a means to quickly and effectively respond to an emergency, and a formal, calendared plan grounded in hard science, for personal longevity.

There are a number of interrelated activities that are critical to effective longevity care:

- Genome risk mapping and risk-related biomarkers

- Integrated nutrition plans

A 60-year-old business owner fell while skiing in Aspen. While at lunch an hour later, he noticed persistent blurry vision in one of his eyes. A guided exam under the direction of his concierge medical practice physician was performed (with the assistance of his spouse) via FaceTime video link. The diagnosis was an acute detached retina. The business owner was instructed to depart immediately for the ER at the local medical center, where he was met by the on-call surgical ophthalmologist. While the patient was en route, the physician spoke directly with the ophthalmologist to relay details of the case, and a PDF copy of the patient's summary medical records was quickly transferred to the emergency room. The patient underwent laser surgery 45 minutes later. He had a full recovery of his vision in a month.

- Lifestyle plans

- Calendared tracking of key metrics

- Response plans to changes in key metrics

Optimally, these activities are supported by technologies such as an integrated scheduling and logistics infrastructure.

Though we could write volumes about longevity care, we'll briefly focus here on the role of biomarkers in genomic risk, long-term health and longevity.

Biomarkers

Very often, the first step in the road to longevity is understanding what biomarkers are and how they can help us live longer. Simply put, biomarkers are data points that are clues to health. Biomarker testing can include blood tests, high-resolution MRIs, cardiac ultrasounds and even blood pressure readings. Most are blood tests used to determine future risk.

A revolution in the use of blood test biomarkers is now underway thanks to the emergence of personal genome sequencing, a process that can reveal a specific future health risk. If an appropriate tracking biomarker can be identified that corresponds to that genomic risk, then a preventive plan can be developed to track and manage the biomarker value to a predetermined goal.

This new model of integrating biomarkers into a genome-based longevity plan is still in its infancy, and almost no providers are incorporating this model in their approach to longevity. While biomarkers and wellness checklists represent a one-size-fits-all approach, a person's unique genome is revolutionary in its singularity.

Genomic mapping and analysis enable the identification of the specific processes that lead to the creation of a future disease state. Once the biomarker is identified that corresponds to that future disease, a detailed protocol can be developed to track and manage the biomarker value to an optimal goal, thus diminishing the patient's lifetime risk for that future illness.

There are three kinds of biomarkers:

1. **DNA-based biomarkers.** These indicate a person's inherited risk for specific diseases. They do not change over time.

2. **Cellular biomarkers.** These are molecules that usually reflect a particular disease state.

3. **Traditional biomarkers.** These are simple indicators of certain physiological functions or parameters.

The use of biomarkers is inherently personalized and unique to each patient. For the testing of biomarkers to be effective, it must be formally calendared according to clearly defined care protocols.

CASE EXAMPLE (PART ONE)

A 54-year-old business owner is very concerned that, like his fore-bearers, he will die of a heart attack by age 60. Thus, the day he turned 61, he was elated. The patient could easily be mistaken for his father or grandfather based on physical appearance and mannerisms, but unlike each of them, he lived past the age of 60. Why didn't he succumb?

Because he was exceptionally proactive in managing his personal health risks. Promoted by his wealth advisor (who had become a trusted friend), he adopted a two-pronged approach by joining a concierge practice. For unpredictable risk like a sudden heart attack, car accident or GI bleed, his first step was ensuring he had immediate access to medical care. He was thus assured that in case of a health care emergency, a capable physician would respond, diagnose and provide immediate, effective treatment. Very importantly, the patient made sure he had a completely objective resource outside of his insurance plan and his local health care system.

His second step was to address his predictable risk. Historically, the only way to assess this was for a physician to ask about family health history. The patient's approach was to leverage new, state-of-the-art techniques to map his genome to identify his future health risks and create a plan to deal with them pre-emptively. Though this approach was somewhat complicated, the result was obvious and positive.

Though this is a real-world story, the truth is that there are many genome-mapping companies. The challenge is converting these results into an actionable personal longevity plan. This success is characterized by the following:

- Relevant and accurate probabilities predicted by the genome

- The identification of the biomarkers that are truly reflective of the specific risks predicted by the genome

- A calendared lifetime plan to formally capture, track and manage the key biomarkers, enabling the patient to achieve optimal long-term goals

A great many predicted diseases can be assessed using relevant biomarkers long before they manifest as a health issue. Additionally, if biomarkers can be returned to normal levels, the risk for that specific disease can be managed. With a plan that regularly checks these biomarkers, the expression of the disease can be prevented.

CASE EXAMPLE (PART TWO)

The response began with the physician summarizing the patient's initial sequencing report, identifying his points of genetic risk and then determining the biomarkers that would reveal the progression of this risk.

This patient's future, unexpressed cardiovascular disease could be seen in his genome. The state of his atherosclerosis itself was visible from his biomarkers. Accordingly, his longevity plan centered on two biomarkers: F2-isoprostanes (F2-IsoPs) and oxidized low-density lipoprotein (LDL), a form of cholesterol that indicates early vascular injury.

The patient's genome revealed an inherited high level of lipoprotein (a), a type of lipoprotein/cholesterol that has been confirmed as a risk factor for coronary heart disease, atherosclerosis, thrombosis and stroke. One in five people has high levels of lipoprotein (a) from birth, based on the genes inherited from his or her parents. To further test the progression of the patient's heart disease, the results of two additional blood tests were analyzed: F2-IsoPs and oxidized LDL. Both biomarkers indicate the progression of inflammation in the body and the corresponding heart attack risk. The patient's levels of both biomarkers were slightly elevated.

In response to the patient's results, the physician immediately put him on a low-carb diet higher in unsaturated fats (the Mediterranean diet) and two OTC supplements: selenium and CoQ10. This combination of supplements has been shown to dramatically decrease heart attack risk. He also started taking niacin. In consultation with a cardiologist, he was also started on a statin (Lipitor) and daily moderate exercise.

When his biomarkers were rechecked at 90 days, they showed the beginning of the trend of diminishment of oxidized LDL and F2-IsoPs. By the six-month mark, they had fallen to levels on the lower end of their normal ranges. He also had ultrasounds of his carotid arteries. The first showed the beginning of significant plaque build-up, but a repeat ultrasound at six months showed that the plaque had stopped progressing. These values attested to the absence of ongoing injury and ensured that his cardiac blood vessels were as healthy as possible. Statistically, his risk for a future heart attack and stroke were much diminished because of these interventions. Calendared follow-up showed that the patient continued to follow the plan, and his subsequent levels of biomarkers remained normal.

There were benefits to the patient's aggressive plan for his own longevity. Once his genome revealed his future probable cause of death, he became highly motivated to understand the implications of elevated biomarkers. As his understanding increased, so did his compliance with the lifestyle plan. He remained committed to his new diet and exercise regimen and his progress was obvious.

Many other people in this patient's life also benefited from his continued health. His wife and family were relieved because he had never been engaged in his own health before. They were quick to conclude that these simple changes would significantly lengthen his life span and, unlike his father, he would see the birth of his grandchildren and other important family milestones.

His co-workers and partners at his firm (who had previously identified the risk of his early death as a major risk to the company he
built) also benefited. His probable longer life will ensure an enduring
legacy for his firm and an opportunity for his partners to grow into
the senior leadership roles he personified.

On a final note, the patient was initially skeptical. He hesitated to
pursue the plan because of the inconvenience of frequent physician office visits and a concern over which physicians would be
accountable for his progress. The latter was a valid concern, as his
personal concierge physician was about to retire and he had yet to
identify any provider who could oversee such a holistic approach
to his health care. His solution was to engage a continuously connected concierge practice to maintain total continuity of his care at
minimal inconvenience.

Genome-based biomarker longevity plans are also important for family
health, as illustrated in the next case example.

CASE EXAMPLE

A couple specifically asked for genomic testing at their concierge
medical practice. Though they were both keen to find out their own
personal health risks, they were also concerned about their potential to pass on to their children newer, more serious diseases, like
Tay-Sachs disease.

In the course of the testing, the father's only identified genetic risk was for common atherosclerosis. However, the mother's genomic analysis identified a very clear risk for potential future cardiac arrhythmias (irregular heartbeat) from a disease called prolonged QT syndrome. Prolonged QT syndrome causes the heart to become electrically unstable at elevated heart rates, which can result in a lethal arrhythmia. It is considered the most common cause of unexplained sudden cardiac death.

Once identified as having the positive gene for prolonged QT syndrome, the mother was referred to a cardio-geneticist who did a full evaluation and concluded that she was indeed at risk for this condition. A stress test revealed electrical instability at high heart rates, and the patient was subsequently started on a beta-blocker, a drug that would limit the ability of her heart to beat at a rate that would force it into electrical instability.

This was probably a lifesaving event for this mother, as she was just beginning to train for a marathon. This could have been quite dangerous for her if she had not been put on the beta-blocker. With strenuous exertion, she could have induced her own electrical instability and had an arrhythmia, and then had a potentially lethal cardiac event. After her initial diagnosis, a formal plan was created for regularly scheduled rechecks with the cardio-geneticist and yearly stress tests.

She also began to carry a hand-held smartphone cardiac monitor. During any period of an elevated heart rate, she tracked herself with the smartphone monitor. This enabled her to control her heart rate and exercise only in the "safe zone."

Through this protocol, she had two means of safeguarding her safety. First, the beta-blocker ensured that her heart never beat too quickly. Second, frequently checking her heart rate with her smartphone cardiac monitor captured her heart's electrical rhythm. Seeing the actual EKG patterns allowed the cardio-geneticist to confirm that she was well-controlled and safe, so long as she took the beta-blocker.

Additionally, her children were now aware of their own risk for this potential future disease, so they were tested for the genetic risk of prolonged QT syndrome. All were negative.

Longevity care and concierge medical practices

As they age, many people think about what they can do to ensure longer, healthy lives. When we look at the different types of concierge medical practices, there are clear distinctions in the involvement of each in longevity care (see Exhibit 6.1). (Again, we include the conventional physician practice for comparison.)

Exhibit 6.1 Longevity Care and Concierge Medical Practices				
Category	Physician Concierge Practice	Private Health Advisory	Continuous Connected Care Practice	Conventional Physician Practice
Genome risk map	Possibly	N/A	Yes	No
Predictive biomarkers	Possibly	N/A	Yes	No
Integrated nutrition plans	Possibly	N/A	Yes	No
Lifestyle plan (e.g., exercise and mental well-being)	Possibly	N/A	Yes	Possibly
Calendared tracking of key metrics	Possibly	N/A	Yes	Limited
Response plan to changes in key metrics	Possibly	N/A	Yes	Limited
Supporting technologies	In person, phone, email, app integrated with scheduling and logistics infrastructure	N/A	Phone, email, app integrated with scheduling and logistics infrastructure	Phone

While longevity care is often a critical service delivered by connected care concierge medical practices, it is not part of private health advisories. Conventional physician practices usually provide only a few of the services and generally do not include biomarker testing.

Within the physician concierge practice category, there is an extremely broad range, with some heavily involved in longevity care and others not touching the matter. When it comes to exclusive physicians, longevity care is often a core service they're providing to their ultra-wealthy patients.

Food for thought

It's a given that you want to live a long, healthy, active life. It's also a given that you want the same for your loved ones. So your key question becomes this:

What are you doing about making sure you and your loved ones have long, healthy, active lives?

You have two options. First, you can manage the process yourself, using available medical resources. For example, you can have your genome mapped. The complication is how you will use this information effectively once you have it. You can adjust your diet and exercise, but this really isn't comprehensive longevity care as we define it.

Alternately, you can work with physicians and care teams that have a deep understanding of longevity care and are actively staying abreast of the latest developments in the field.

Currently, the second option is available primarily through an exclusive concierge physician relationship, continuously connected care practices and the rare physician concierge practice.

The people driving concierge medicine want better health care and have the means to fund this desire. At the same time, concierge medical practices are evolving. This makes it useful to understand how and why the wealthy and—in particular—the ultra-wealthy are using concierge medicine.

CHAPTER 7

In the Service of the Ultra-Wealthy

Because the ultra-wealthy have been early adopters of concierge medicine, it's helpful to understand how and why they use it. While many ultra-wealthy live rarefied lives, they also face medical challenges common to us all, regardless of how luxurious their surroundings may be.

In his chapter, we'll look at two medical care requirements fairly unique to the ultra-wealthy (and their guests): ensuring high-quality medical care on private islands and remote ranches, and obtaining exceptional health care when the patient is a truly global citizen.

Private islands, residences and ranches

There are no more than 2,000 islands close to land in politically stable locations where development is permitted. People who own private islands often surmount almost innumerable obstacles, ranging from basic infra-

On the family's private island, the 8-year-old daughter of a wealthy business founder awoke crying with an earache and fever over the weekend. The parents called their concierge medical practice's on-call physician, and the mother examined the child's ear with a video-linked otoscope in the island clinic established by the medical practice.

The child was diagnosed with a middle-ear infection and started on antibiotics and pain medication from the on-site clinic pharmacy. The daughter's progress was closely tracked, and no off-island travel was necessary. The concierge medical practice transferred records of the case, including a picture of the child's infected eardrum, to the child's pediatrician when the family returned to the United States.

structure (electricity and water) to professional island management staff and regularly chartered food delivery. Like remote ranches, the principal benefit to island owners is privacy, a commodity not easily available to them in their regular public lives. However, that privacy has an additional significant cost: lack of access to health care when needed.

Concierge medical practices have been extensively involved in providing medical care to the owners, staff and guests of private islands and other isolated locations. In these environments, it's critical to be able to effectively treat or stabilize a new problem, as access to other modern medical facilities means unscheduled travel, which means time delays.

For example, when a guest on an island accidentally slices a portion of her ankle off while hiking, being able to quickly clean the exposed skin, reposition the tissue and use surgical glue to secure it more permanently results in the ankle wound's healing without any complications or loss of function. This all happens under the supervision of talented telemedical physicians and requires no off-island travel.

CASE EXAMPLE

An ultra-wealthy matriarch experienced sudden shortness of breath upon arrival at her ranch in Mexico. She had just flown back to North America from Asia (a 16-hour flight).

The patient went to the telemedical clinic on the ranch, where she was evaluated via a FaceTime interview. The information about her recent long flight and medical history led the on-call emergency physician to consider the possibility that a deep vein blood clot had migrated to her lungs (pulmonary embolus).

Her oxygen and heart rate were subsequently tested through a pulse oximeter, which found that her oxygen saturation had diminished to well-below-normal values. She was immediately given an injection of a blood thinner as well as an aspirin tablet to augment her treatment. Her summarized medical records were reviewed in anticipation of a rapid evacuation.

The patient was subsequently evacuated to the U.S. and then transported by private ambulance to a leading hospital with acclaimed pulmonary specialists. The patient's medical records were sent to the emergency room, and her concierge medical practice physician briefed the emergency physician on her condition prior to her arrival. A subsequent chest CT scan showed the presence of a single, large, isolated blood clot in her right lung.

Admitted to a monitored bed in the hospital, she did quite well, with her oxygen saturation returning to normal on the second day. While in the hospital, she was started on a more permanent anticoagulant, and then she completed a seven-day recovery at home. Ten days after this life-threatening event, the patient's pulmonologist cleared her for the short flight back to the ranch, where her ongoing recovery was closely tracked by the on-call physician team. Returning to the U.S. four weeks later, the patient completed her calendared care plan. A recheck showed she was effectively anticoagulated, and a repeat CT scan of her chest 60 days later showed complete resolution of her pulmonary embolus.

Global citizenship

Health care is a major concern among families with multiple international residences. It is not uncommon for a family to have just a single relationship with one primary physician or hospital at one of their principal residences. Complications arise when a family member has an acute medical issue at a different residence or while traveling. Rarely are there protocols in place for the primary physician to ensure that the patient's records are completely ready for transfer on a moment's notice to another facility beyond the patient's home hospital. Even worse, the patient may not know the best facility at this other location and may waste critical response time traveling to a local facility, only to find out that it is unequipped to treat them effectively.

Without a centralized, globally aware medical practice that is available 24/7, the management of acute medical problems can easily become disorganized and ineffective. Without a physician to make a high-quality referral and act as a health advocate, the patient risks getting "lost" in an unfamiliar health care system. Many global citizens have the personal resources to pay for the "best of everything" everywhere they go. Paradoxically, the sole exception to this rule is their personal health care, which does not follow them as they travel and is often incomplete as a result. This painful reality is particularly true for older patients with chronic conditions, for whom continuity of care is crucial for the best outcome.

CASE EXAMPLE

An extremely successful business owner experienced the new on-set of atrial fibrillation (a common cardiac arrhythmia) at age 64. Highly motivated to continue his busy personal and professional lifestyle, he was keen that this new diagnosis would in no way im-pair his current activities, which included extensive international travel pursuing his business and recreational interests.

The patient's cardiologist, a founding partner in a general cardiolo-gy practice, insisted that the patient's atrial fibrillation be managed in a series of office visits. This was unworkable for the patient and his busy lifestyle, so he asked his concierge medical practice to arrange for a second opinion with a leading arrhythmia cardiologist.

The month before that appointment, the patient was provided with a pocket-sized cardiac rhythm monitor. This monitor was paired to his smartphone, and the patient was taught how to easily capture his cardiac rhythm twice a day and send it to his concierge medical practice. This data was organized into a summary report for a sec-ond opinion by a cardiologist specializing in the management of the atrial fibrillation.

During the patient's appointment, the arrhythmia specialist refer-enced the 30 days of arrhythmia data and subsequently adjusted the patient's medications, thus maximizing the patient's rate con-trol. Thirty days of subsequent daily EKGs confirmed that the pa-tient was optimally managed.

The patient was able to maintain his very busy lifestyle as a business owner and continue his international travel schedule with the knowledge that his cardiac rhythm was being monitored and that, if needed, his concierge medical practice could quickly arrange a rapid referral and/or emergency care at the best hospital in each of his frequent business destinations, which included Beijing, Istanbul, Mumbai, Tokyo, Kuala Lumpur and Singapore, to name but a few.

The patient, who was a very numbers-driven person, became engaged in and enthusiastic about his care from knowing that his management was based on hard data and that he himself was playing a key role in his own optimal health.

There are indeed many ways to legally avoid paying taxes. One approach is to become a perpetual tourist (also known as a perpetual traveler). By not spending very much time in any jurisdiction, a person can legitimately avoid paying taxes anywhere while enjoying an enduring increase in personal freedom. However, that advantage has a downside, as we see in the next case example.

CASE EXAMPLE

A billionaire perpetual tourist wanted a single-family office after having determined that the private banks he was relying on were both too expensive and inadequate for his expectations. His primary concern was being able to access all his financial information and elite professional talent on an anytime, anywhere basis. Based on his requirements, the answer for him was a near-virtual single-family office.

With the same intention, the billionaire, now into his early 70s, was very concerned about being able to receive the finest medical care wherever he was. Additionally, he was very concerned about ensuring he had a long and rewarding life. There are only a couple of ways to address these goals: connected care or a private personal physician.

He chose to hire two exceptionally capable private physicians. Alternating their duties, one physician is in constant attendance of the patient's entourage and equipped with a wide array of diagnostic and treatment resources. The two physicians have also prearranged a transfer protocol for their patient at his home medical center in the U.S.

In our experience, a large percentage of Super Rich families are very concerned about the quality and reliability of the health care they receive. Complicating this situation is the fact that a significant number of their extended family members and personal business interests are scattered around the globe. For some of them, the solution is to travel with their own world-class physician and medical support staff, as the next case example shows.

CASE EXAMPLE

A globe-spanning family with commercial interests in 32 countries created its very own mobile mini-hospital. It has six full-time physicians on staff: two internists, an ER physician, a pediatrician, a hematologist and a cardiologist.

In addition, there is an eight-member support staff team consisting of nurses and physician assistants. A dietician (who is also an award-winning chef) and two personal trainers (who can double as nurses) are adjuncts to the health care team.

The family owns four very large multi-residence compounds in different parts of the world. There is a fully equipped medical clinic at each location. There are also extensive medical capabilities aboard all of their private jets and their two yachts. A physician always travels with the matriarch or patriarch as well as family members when they travel. All family members can readily access the health care team, as there is a physician on call and immediately available 24/7.

At every location, family members have easy access to the physician staff at local high-caliber medical centers when needed. The family also has a number of world-renowned specialists on permanent retainer, with the ability to access them and their associated medical institutions on demand.

This family's health care solution is probably the ultimate level of concierge medical care. Many heads of state would be hard-pressed to match the high-quality health care resources and operating support available to this Super Rich family. However, let's not forget that the family is personally paying for this level of medical care, and the cost runs into the millions annually. Then again, when exceptional health care is a top priority and the fortune at risk numbers into the billions, a few million dollars a year proves to be a very solid investment.

It's clear from these case examples that the ultra-wealthy are embracing concierge medicine. We see this trend especially when single-family offices are looking at health care.

Single-family offices and concierge medicine

Broadly speaking, a single-family office is an organizational structure that manages the financial and personal affairs of one ultra-wealthy family. Because a single-family office is driven purely by the needs and preferences of the underlying family, there's no standard for how one should be structured. For instance, some single-family offices are extremely lean enterprises that focus exclusively on investing, with a small expert staff, while others are robust organizations with in-house staff, numerous vendor relationships and a broad platform of services. This disparity means that it's difficult to establish hard-and-fast criteria for how a single-family office should be defined other than its core dedication to its client.

Most single-family offices tend to provide two principal categories of services: wealth management and family support. Under the umbrella of wealth management, we often find investment management and tax planning. Simultaneously, we often see administrative and lifestyle services under the category of family support services. Under the banner of lifestyle services, we often find some version of concierge medicine.

Over the years, concierge medicine has become increasingly important to most single-family offices (see Exhibit 7.1). While these are different samples of single-family offices, there's a pronounced trend to engage concierge medical practices. Furthermore, concierge medicine will likely be of even greater interest to the ultra-wealthy across the spectrum as the health care landscape continues to change.

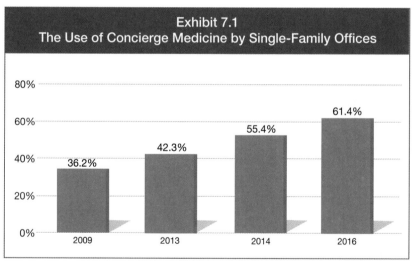

Exhibit 7.1
The Use of Concierge Medicine by Single-Family Offices

2009: N = 376 single-family office senior executives.   2013: N = 78 single-family office senior executives.
2014: N = 83 single-family office senior executives.   2015: N = 101 single-family office senior executives.
Source: AES Nation.

Food for thought

Having a great deal of money can readily translate into being able to access the finest in health care, but you don't need to be ultra-wealthy or even that rich to afford some version of concierge medicine. The case examples in this chapter were clearly a little extreme, but they highlighted the two types of concierge medical practices frequently engaged by the ultra-wealthy: the continuously connected care and personally exclusive physician concierge medical practices.

So consider these questions:

If money were no object, how likely would you be to become a patient of one of these two types of concierge medical practices?

What about each of these types of concierge medical practices appeals to you? What doesn't thrill you?

Let's presume you are not ultra-wealthy. You probably realize that high-quality concierge medicine is available today at many price points, ranging from an annual cost of a couple of thousand dollars for a local office-based physician or medical center-affiliated physician, to tens of thousands of dollars for a continuously connected concierge practice, up to millions of dollars for exclusive personal physicians. So now ask:

What type of concierge medical practice is starting to make sense for you and your loved ones?

Without question, the cost of concierge medicine is a consideration for most people and impacts their choice of concierge medical practice.

At the same time, there are a number of possible ways to mitigate the costs of using a concierge medical resource through wealth management solutions, the topic of the next chapter.

CHAPTER 8

Wealth Management and Concierge Medicine

Clearly, the world of medical care is changing and the pace of change is likely to accelerate. Our traditional health care system is very unlikely to address the growing potential for people to get poor care. For those who are concerned and can afford it, concierge medicine is a viable solution. However, the cost of high-quality concierge medicine ranges extensively.

If you are worth billions or even tens of millions and you have liquidity, you can probably pay out of pocket for concierge medicine as well as for cutting-edge diagnostics and treatments. If you are not, there are financial and legal strategies you can use to address the costs.

Longevity planning means that modifications to financial and legal plans are often needed. These issues are becoming very real and need to be addressed:

At 2:00 a.m. in a Beijing hotel room,

a business owner experienced severe chest pain and called his concierge physician's hotline. Within five minutes he was treated with nitroglycerin, aspirin and a beta-blocker from his personal prescription medical kit. While his chest pain was easing, his concierge care team coordinated his transportation to the only hospital with a 24-hour cardiac catheter lab and a Western-trained cardiologist. En route, the patient's baseline EKG and records were sent to the hospital, and the concierge physician conferred directly with the cardiology team there. At 3:15 a.m., he underwent a successful angioplasty. Four days later, he was airlifted to his home hospital in Boston, with his family closely informed every step of the way. He suffered no permanent cardiac injury and was fully recovered in two weeks.

- Ensuring you do not run out of money now that you and your loved ones may live much longer than expected, even past 100

- Adjusting the timing on the transfer of ownership and control of the family business, given that the principal may live longer than expected

- Paying for what is likely to be very expensive medical care so that you or loved ones can continue to have an extended healthy life

There are many implications—societal, business and family—of an extended and productive life. Consequently, some of the foremost wealth managers, accountants and attorneys are working with families to make certain their financial and legal worlds are in order and benefiting from high-quality concierge medicine. As wealth management is very often center stage in this process, let's begin by defining what it is.

Wealth management

The term "wealth management" is thrown around plenty in the boardrooms of private client firms, in trade and mainstream articles, and by financial advisors in front of clients. Still, most professionals would be hard-pressed to actually define the term with any degree of precision.

Wealth management is straightforward. From the affluent individual's perspective, it is simply the art and science of solving financial challenges and enhancing his or her financial situation.

From a financial professional's perspective, wealth management is the ability of an advisor or advisory team to deliver a full range of financial services and products to an affluent client in a consultative way. By being consultative, wealth managers are truly client-centered. A good wealth manager meets a client without any supposition about what financial products or services are appropriate for that individual.

While it is common for an individual to go to a wealth manager to address a particular need (investment management, say), the consultative wealth manager's overriding objective is to understand the person and find out what is important and why. Then the wealth manager can bring in the appropriate experts and provide the appropriate financial products.

In sum:

Wealth management is the consultative process of meeting the needs and wants of clients by providing the appropriate financial products and services.

Wealth management entails coordinating a team of experts to address the needs and wants of clients.

High-quality concierge medicine is part of a number of different personal financial scenarios. In each scenario, there are various wealth management solutions that might be applicable.

Consider a wealthy family with a net worth in excess of $100 million. The complication is that the money is tied up in the family business. This presents a financial risk if a family member requires state-of-the-art treatments that are available only in a foreign country. Additionally, if the treatments go well, there are going to be substantial costs for rehabilitation.

In this case, the use of genomic testing and biomarkers can be instrumental in preserving the family business while making sure the loved one gets the best medical care possible. In this scenario, there are many wealth management solutions that can be used, such as a captive insurance company to address health care.

Simply put, captive insurance companies are ways businesses can tax-efficiently self-insure. Without question, there are many potential tax benefits for firms using captive insurance companies. The error is when they're used inappropriately or incorrectly. If structured properly, captive insurance companies can be adroitly used to manage health care risks, including paying for concierge medicine. Moreover, if the claims are not considerable, there potentially are tax benefits for the owners of the captive insurance company—the owners of the company being insured.

Another scenario is when individuals, due to longer and more active lives, potentially run out of money. With medical costs likely to continue to rise and with age working against you, you need the funds to ensure a long, well-lived life. A potential solution is to manage your financial assets in a way that takes into account a much longer life span. One way the Super Rich are approaching this matter is by using private placement life insurance.

For investors, it's really about what they walk away with, not necessarily how much they earn. A great-performing investment can become very mediocre once taxes are taken into account. However, there are ways of mitigating the tax bite from a variety of different types of investments.

For over two decades, one of the best-kept secrets in tax planning has been private placement life insurance, which makes it possible for an investor to capture returns tax-free. A tremendous appeal of private placement life insurance is that the investment options can be tailored to an investor's needs and the cost of insurance per dollar of coverage is much reduced. With proper planning, the cash value appreciation and insurance coverage can also escape gift and estate taxes. It can also often be structured to provide world-class creditor protection.

Captive insurance companies and private placement life insurance are two of a number of possible wealth management solutions that can be used to address the current and future financial needs, wants and preferences of affluent concierge medical patients.

Estate planning

Another implication of longer life spans due to longevity planning is that people have to rethink their estate plans. With respect to estate planning—especially for the wealthy—the potential to live much longer is becoming a potential minefield for the families as well as their wealth managers and tax experts. Specifically, more significant issues develop for high-net-worth families in how and when to transfer assets to subsequent generations.

Among wealthy families, a critical question becomes *"When does the next generation get to benefit and control the assets they are intended to have?"* If successful business owners, for instance, are living past 100 thanks to medical advances, when do the inheritors take control of family-owned and managed companies? In their 70s? 80s? 90s? If the families do not think through the possibilities, potentially disastrous confrontations could arise.

Controlling wealth until death is a common desire among many self-made millionaires. However, this thinking can lead to poor estate planning, especially when the people involved live a long, long time. When the wealth holders are living a very long time, it's probably their responsibility to construct estate plans that clearly spell out what's to happen, and many times, it's wise to transfer assets before death. Transferring assets before death solves lots of possible problems, such as family disputes and lawsuits, and assets strangely disappearing. Because of the possibility of dementia or older wealth holders' being exploited by advisors, staff or family members, shifting some of the wealth before death can be very beneficial for all involved.

If you have considerable wealth and the issue is not outliving your money, you might find yourself confronted with a different set of complications. There are potentially unprecedented wealth transfer considerations arising from seriously extended life spans.

Caveat emptor

With concierge medicine booming (see the next chapter) and longevity planning in particular garnering tremendous interest, high-caliber wealth managers and aligned professionals are going to play critical supporting roles. The expertise of talented and skilled wealth managers can be crucial to enabling those who are not stratospherically wealthy to afford the finest concierge medical practices and any diagnostic or treatment regime.

Because of the solid and growing appeal of longevity planning, many astute financial and legal professionals are becoming adept at the many wealth management solutions that can be employed to address its implications. For example, there are many ways private placement life insurance can prove beneficial, from enhancing investment returns to being the funding vehicle for sophisticated deferred compensation arrangements to being a core part of a wealthy individual's life insurance portfolio intended to pay estate taxes.

The real conundrum you face as you look to leverage wealth management solutions as part of protecting your most precious assets—your and your family's health and well-being—is mistakenly putting your trust in Pretenders and Predators.

Pretenders are not bad people. On the contrary, these financial advisors are well-meaning and want to do an excellent job for you. The complication is that they are just not up to the task. We have found that most of the time, the conundrum with Pretenders is that they don't know what *they don't know—and there's a lot they don't know.*

Pretenders might be aware of a concept, but they lack the insight and knowledge to deliver exceptional results. Consider the wealth management solutions we just highlighted—captive insurance companies and private placement life insurance.

In a survey of 803 financial advisors, about half of them said they *know* about captive insurance companies (see Exhibit 8.1). However, less than

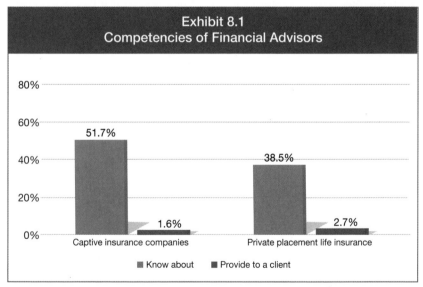

N = 803 financial advisors.
Source: *Becoming Seriously Wealthy: How to Harness the Strategies of the Super Rich and Ultra-Wealthy Business Owners,* 2017.

2 percent said they *provide* the solution to a client. Similarly, almost two out of five financial advisors reported knowing about private placement life insurance, but less than 3 percent of the financial advisors surveyed have ever provided this solution to a client.

Predators are likely to be much more destructive to your wealth than Pretenders. Why? Predators are criminals. They are con artists and hustlers using guile, deception and finesse to illegally separate you from your money while posing as trusted advisors. They create a world of artifice composed of enchanting money myths and financial fantasies.

When it comes to the overlap of wealth management and concierge medicine, you can expect Predators to become more and more prevalent. With the prospect of people's long, healthy lives, cunning criminals will devise numerous scams and subterfuges aimed at reinforcing your beliefs while picking your pockets.

The following are some criteria that can help you select wealth managers and other professionals who can help you address the financial and legal consequences of longevity planning and paying for state-of-the-art health care like concierge medicine.

Criterion #1: Proven integrity

Integrity is at the very top of the list for a very good reason: To protect and enhance your wealth, wealth managers must be scrupulously honest.

Thus, you must take care when evaluating a wealth manager. It can be helpful to ask any wealth manager you consider working with these two questions:

1. Under what conditions would you fire a client?

2. What will you NOT do?

These questions can help you gain perspective on the moral compass of a wealth manager you are considering.

Criterion #2: Operational transparency

It's essential to select a wealth manager who is completely open and forthright with you. This takes a number of forms, including being very clear about his or her compensation arrangements and your right to obtain second opinions (see below).

Criterion #3: Extensive technical expertise

Everyone wants to work with a top-notch professional. You need to consider numerous factors to effectively evaluate the technical competencies of wealth managers, such as the following:

• Educational background

• Professional experience

- Professional licenses and designations

- Associations with industry organizations

- Publications and speaking engagements

- Recognition from peers in the financial and legal communities

Criterion #4: Access to niche experts

Wealth managers are not walking encyclopedias. They often need to bring in specialists who are experts in particular niches, such as captive insurance companies. Be aware of the network of niche experts available to wealth managers you consider.

Criterion #5: Experience integrating wealth management solutions with concierge medicine

Creative professionals are increasingly finding innovative ways to marry wealth management with concierge medicine. You are best-served if the wealth manager or a specialist he or she works with has experience with various wealth management solutions and, better still, has experience using them in the context of concierge medicine—especially longevity planning.

By employing these criteria, you meaningfully boost your chances of avoiding both Pretenders and Predators. In addition, you can employ an approach used extensively by the Super Rich: getting financial and legal second opinions.

Without question, one of the best ways to deal with a possible economically destructive situation about which you are just "not completely sure" or you "feel a little uncertain" is to get a second opinion. Under these circumstances, not only is it often a wise move to get a second opinion before taking action, but it is probably also a wise move to go this route even if you have already taken action and are a little bit unsure and anxious. This gives you the opportunity to correct mistakes or use wealth management solutions that can produce superior results.

Food for thought

Carefully and proactively integrating wealth management into some of your thinking when it comes to concierge medicine can prove very worthwhile. As we discussed, the main issues revolve around being able to always afford the best health care and the prospect of outliving your money. You therefore want to consider the following three questions:

How concerned are you about the costs of concierge medicine, cutting-edge medical diagnosis and treatment, and possibly running out of money because you are living past 100?

If you are concerned about any of these issues, are you working with a high-caliber wealth manager who is knowledgeable about concierge medicine and can help you take steps to ensure—as best as possible—that you can afford the health care you want for yourself and your loved ones?

If you have any doubts about getting the best financial advice, are you able to seek out a second opinion?

For most people—even very wealthy people—the ability to use wealth management solutions to constructively address the costs of health care can be tremendous. But being able to do so depends on working with a stellar wealth manager.

CHAPTER 9

The Future of Concierge Medicine

There is little question that concierge medicine is a growth industry. Just consider the following equation incorporating several of the most recent and sustained trends in health care:

An increasingly turbulent health care system that often ineffectively delivers on the promise of quality patient care

+

An increasing number of primary care physicians rejecting the current "seven-minute medicine" physician/employee practice model to restore time and commitment in caring for their patients

+

New, sometimes hard-to-access, lifesaving technologies

+

An expanding cohort of potential patients who can afford and are willing to pay for exceptional health care

=

A substantial and enduring yearly increase in the number of concierge medical practices

A 57-year-old CFO wakes up in a hotel room to find the left side of his face paralyzed. Assuming it's a stroke, he contacts his concierge physician. The physician examines him via smartphone video and rules out a stroke but confirms a diagnosis of Bell's palsy—a temporary paralysis of a facial nerve. The patient is immediately started on two medications from his personal medical kit and a same-day appointment is made with a top neurologist.

While he completes his meetings, his concierge medical practice collects and condenses all relevant medical records for his follow-up appointment back home in New York. Within five weeks, the paralysis is resolved.

Though this concierge practice trend started among independent community physicians, it's very telling that it has now spread to the primary care staffs of major medical centers. They recognize that this movement is not going away and are now actively seeking to recruit the physician talent they need to lock in these patients for the long term.

Hospitals adopting concierge medicine to cultivate wealthy patients

Practicing physicians and smaller medical institutions are driving most of concierge health care today. However, there are strong indications that many hospitals have embraced the idea of establishing their own concierge medical practices. For example, the third-oldest general hospital in the country, Massachusetts General Hospital, recently decided to quietly open a concierge health care office for its affluent patients. Mass General Hospital and other hospitals recognize that by ignoring the concierge medicine trend, they are also ignoring a significant revenue opportunity.

The economic and professional rationale for hospitals to offer concierge medical services is the same as for many primary care physicians: a desire to be financially rewarded for superior clinical performance. There are potentially enormous benefits to a hospital successfully offering concierge medical care. Besides a new revenue stream, these in-house programs can offer state-of-the-art medical assessments and treatments. Using these innovations in their patient acquisition and branding efforts, medical centers can build a reputation for excellence without the usual massive overhead and limited profitability inherent in the rest of their patient population. As part of this effort, the effective use of high-quality telemedicine is a powerful attractant, as is the adoption of long-term personal longevity care plans.

It's also important to keep in mind that the number of wealthy patients is growing dramatically. These patients face a conundrum: They want the best and latest medical innovations, but they are forced into a system that cannot provide them. This mismatch of well-funded demand and relative scarcity is driving the move by many hospitals toward concierge medicine.

The wealthy want the latest and most innovative medical treatments, such as immunotherapy to treat cancer or stem cell infusions for cardiac recovery, and they will always be willing to pay whatever they need to receive these treatments. Moreover, they want to know what diseases or illnesses are most likely to befall them in the future, thus driving the need for genome- and biomarker-based longevity care.

Beyond conventional print and web marketing, there are multiple ways elite hospitals are attracting wealthy patients today. In the near term, these approaches will likely continue and become more refined. With more hospitals focusing on the wealthy, coupled with the evolution of concierge health care, cultivating high-net-worth patients will become much more competitive. Changing dynamics and increasing competition are going to demand more targeted and insightful approaches.

Awareness of cutting-edge treatments

The increasingly global nature of medicine combined with the speed of communication means that it is now possible to learn about cutting-edge treatments from all over the world almost instantly. This access to information about new treatments, coupled with the fact that the concierge model often gives physicians more time to keep abreast of developments in their field, means that widespread awareness of medical innovations is emerging as a pronounced movement. With more time away from paperwork and a less grueling patient load, concierge physicians are more aware of major treatment advances and use this expertise as a way to differentiate their practices from others. This is both a trend and a key benefit of concierge medical practices.

Though there is a wide range in how innovatively concierge medical practices operate, the more personalized nature of concierge medicine tends to increase the probability that their patients will receive the most current treatments. It's important to be cognizant of this when evaluating a potential concierge medical practice for yourself and your family.

The best concierge medical practices are aware of medical innovations across multiple specialties, including specialties outside the primary physician's core expertise. A great concierge practice usually has some version of a dedicated researcher or team that is looking across all specialties for innovations and emerging treatments.

The exciting part of this trend is that it encompasses innovations that are immediately available to people everywhere, as well as trends for specific issues. The best concierge medical practices share cutting-edge information and emerging treatment options with patients affected by both common conditions and exceedingly rare diseases.

These medical care innovations tend to fall into three categories: treatments available now over the counter, treatments accessible through a physician now and treatments available through a physician later (see Exhibit 9.1).

		Actionable	
Exhibit 9.1 Medical Innovations			
		Now	*Later*
Accessible	*Over the counter*	Example: selenium and CoQ10 supplements	
	Through a physician	Example: latest artificial disc replacement technology and stem cell joint regeneration	Example: stem cell treatment for multiple sclerosis

Innovations available over the counter now encompass most simple, sensible lifestyle habits, like regular exercise and a healthy diet. However, there are some others that are simple yet not quite so obvious.

A clear example of this sort of innovation is daily selenium and CoQ10 supplementation. These are two credible supplements available at any pharmacy, but when taken together, their positive effects are magnified. On their own, these supplements assist cells in clearing away the damage caused by oxidative stress—damage caused by a lack of sleep, a poor diet, too much alcohol and other habits of an unhealthy lifestyle. When taken in combination, they have a multiplicative effect on cells' ability to clear away free radicals (the product of oxidative stress).

This has huge implications for longevity and health because every cell in the body can be harmed by oxidative stress. When unmanaged, oxidative stress forces your cells to repair and replicate themselves at an increased frequency. The cells most at risk are also the most critical for successful aging; among them are the neurons in your brain, the myocytes in your heart and the nephrons in your kidneys.

Being able to minimize or mitigate oxidative stress with a scientifically credible series of supplements is something any patient can do with the recommendation of a physician, and it can have a profoundly positive effect on one's ability to protect his or her body from the effects of inflammation. The key to leveraging these innovations successfully is having a physician who can evaluate their medical efficacy and then apply them effectively to a patient's life.

Innovations accessible through a doctor now encompass treatments and procedures that not every patient may need but are nonetheless intensely beneficial to those suffering from the specific conditions these innovations address.

The classic example of this is the artificial disc replacement (ADR). This has been a long-standing procedure, roughly a decade old, where patients with herniated or otherwise damaged spinal discs get new discs made from plastic or other materials. The ADR has been a tremendous advance for many people with back pain and injuries, as spinal fusions were previously the only available treatment for many disc issues. With each passing year, there has been a better technology—better artificial discs. This means that not all artificial discs are created equal, even though different ones may be available. A first-generation artificial disc is nowhere near as good as a fifth-generation artificial disc, and a great concierge practice will know or find out the latest, most credible and most frequently recommended device.

In the same vein, there are credible stem cell therapies for other orthopedic issues. Stem cell treatment for joint degeneration consists of extracting and concentrating stem cells from the patient's own fat and then injecting them into the injured joint, where they will rebuild the joint with brand-new tissue. Though considered more cutting edge, there are stem cell clinics outside the U.S. that have been treating joint degeneration successfully. A good concierge medical practice will make the effort to find out where the most credible stem cell facilities and physicians are, and then close the treatment loop by making the referral.

For all immediately available treatments accessible through physicians, like artificial discs and stem cell therapy, the best concierge practices will find out what the state of practice is both in the U.S. and abroad, and actively search for procedures that are not yet FDA-approved but may be EU-approved (as in the case of specific stem cell therapies). Additionally, they will ensure that the patient actually receives the cutting-edge treatment by making the proper referrals and tracking the patient's progress.

CASE EXAMPLE

A 64-year-old man had a known history of an enlarged prostate (benign prostatic hypertrophy) and it was becoming a significant problem, as it was disrupting his sleep. His bladder capacity was shrinking to the point where he was getting up every two hours in the night. As a result, he was not getting any true, deeply restorative recovery sleep, and his work performance was suffering.

He was told by his regular urologist that there was not much more that could be done beyond starting him on Cialis, a therapy that is quite valid and common. However, this patient did not want to take a daily medication that came with side effects. He had a family history of heart disease and was very concerned about the precautions given to Cialis users with heart disease.

> Given his desire to avoid Cialis, his concierge medical practice undertook a nationwide search for the best procedures to restore normal bladder function. Ultimately, the patient had a minimally invasive surgery at a top teaching hospital. His bladder function was restored, allowing him to sleep and restoring his performance both at work and in his personal life.

Innovations available through a physician later often address serious and complex diseases, like cancer, end-stage multiple sclerosis and other autoimmune diseases. There are many powerful advances that will become available through physicians to patients who suffer from these conditions.

A prime example of this is a new multiple sclerosis treatment protocol being tested through a U.S. and U.K. research partnership. The treatment consists of retrieving stem cells from the patient's bone marrow, and then subsequently using a modified chemotherapy protocol to wipe out the white blood cells of the patient's immune system—the same immune system that has been attacking the patient's own body. When all of the patient's white blood cells are wiped out, the patient's immune system "forgets" that it was programmed to attack normal cells—in the case of multiple sclerosis, healthy neurons—and the immune system can then be "rebuilt" to normal function through the infusion of the previously collected stem cells.

For a severe autoimmune disease like multiple sclerosis, the effect is extraordinary. Once the patient's immune system "forgets" that it targeted healthy cells, the disease either stops progressing or begins to reverse. No longer under assault, healthy cells begin to repair themselves using some of the newly infused stem cells. In one trial, there was an 85 percent success rate with this therapy. It's brand-new and absolutely cutting-edge research that has profound implications and potential for patients suffering from not just multiple sclerosis but also any type of autoimmune disease.

A good concierge medical practice should be aware of these cutting-edge therapies so it can make the referrals and improve the quality of life for patients who suffer from serious, complex diseases. At a minimum, a concierge medical practice should have a qualified, expert researcher staff member devoted to tracking scientific periodicals so it can identify the latest valid therapies on behalf of patients with complex diseases. This allows patients suffering from complex diseases to try new treatments, get evaluated by field leaders and take part in studies that test new advances in their diseases. The concierge practice should not just be committed to providing care, but it should also be committed to seeking out the innovations that will transform patients' lives for the better.

Access to this level of innovation has a direct impact on the lives of patients. Awareness of cutting-edge treatments and the ability to connect patients to them are key parts of the best concierge practices. This trend will continue to grow as concierge medicine becomes more widespread.

Leveraging personal technologies

When people feel sick or have identified some health issues, they usually want answers as quickly as possible. For some, the anxiety of not knowing the cause of their illness can be quite overwhelming. This has led to a relatively new but widespread practice: sick people looking for a diagnosis of their symptoms on the Internet. Occasionally, the web does deliver an accurate diagnosis, but more commonly, misdirection and confusion ensue, often leading to a misdiagnosis and unnecessary delay.

These troubling situations can be avoided if a patient has a responsive concierge physician or telemedical doctor who is immediately available. For the hypochondriac or particularly anxious patient, rapid access to a physician to describe a problem, reach a working diagnosis and receive reassurance that the problem is not the "blood cancer" they have read about on the Internet is truly valuable, saving them hours or days of unnecessary anxiety and fear.

Across the concierge medicine industry, the use of smartphone apps is becoming more common, as they are an easy and efficient way to communicate and coordinate health care. Someday soon, all concierge medical practices will have their own app that will enable patients to talk directly to physicians or care team members, or simply schedule a visit or call at a mutually convenient time (instead of getting stuck on hold).

These same apps will also revolutionize the way chronic diseases like hypertension, depression, atrial fibrillation and diabetes are tracked and managed. When an app is integrated with a Bluetooth-connected monitor, a patient's smartphone captures and delivers data to the concierge medical care team, and the team can act upon it immediately and continuously for the benefit of the patient.

For the global continuously connected concierge medical practice, a geo-location tool within its app will be a standard feature. With this geospatial capability, the physicians and health care team can see exactly where the patient is physically located. The home office team can then immediately overlay a grid of the best local doctors, pharmacies and hospitals. The process is successfully closed when the patient receives driving directions and instructions directly on his or her phone.

We predict that within ten years, all of us, when taken ill, will contact an expert resource (an experienced physician, a software-supported nurse or possibly even a clinical artificial intelligence) to triage our health care problem, identify the possible diagnoses and begin treatment outside the office, emergency room or clinic. Our connectivity will also ensure close follow-up. And the exceptions that require higher levels of care will be identified early and treated more accurately and aggressively than they are now.

The boom in medical tourism

In some cases, accessing the precisely right treatment may involve travel across the nation or around the world, a phenomenon known as medical tourism. In 2015, medical tourism—travel to a particular facility for a particular medical procedure or treatment—generated between $60 billion and $70 billion. Within five years, it's very likely that number will double or possibly triple.

The ease of international travel, coupled with the emergence of private-pay modern health care services (both in the U.S. and abroad), has fostered the explosive growth of medical tourism. There are three kinds of medical tourists:

1. Those seeking modern medical care in the U.S.

2. Those seeking cutting-edge treatments available only abroad

3. Those seeking to save money on an expensive procedure

By far the biggest cohort is people coming to the U.S. for a higher level of care than is available in their home country. Virtually every country with a social medical system has patients who are unhappy with the wait involved or the obsolescence of the state treatment most commonly applied to their conditions—usually cancer, orthopedic issues or heart disease.

In reply to this demand, major brand-name medical systems in the U.S. have expanded in this market by establishing international medical offices whose primary jobs are to facilitate the visit of wealthier-than-average foreigners and to ensure these patients' satisfaction and future referral business.

Americans are also among international medical tourists. The wealthy among them leave the U.S. for cutting-edge treatments (some credible, some not) that are available only abroad. The FDA rarely approves the treatments, so caution is advised in this endeavor. There are both credible providers and clinically effective treatments available abroad. There are also quacks who pose as credible.

Less-wealthy Americans may also travel for medical care. Innovative surgical, dental and cosmetic procedures are expensive in the U.S., and for people with a high-deductible health insurance policy (or no insurance at all), this is a viable option. Again, caution is advised in the selection and qualification of any overseas providers.

A special note on the subject of stem cells when discussing medical tourism: Many credible and effective stem cell therapies have been identified and published by the medical research community. Some of the results have been nothing short of miraculous. Unfortunately, hope for a miracle has misled many people into looking abroad for the same therapies described in the published science. These therapies do exist, but "buyer beware" is the best place to ground your thinking before beginning the search.

CASE EXAMPLE

An active matriarch was experiencing debilitating chronic knee pain because of advanced osteoarthritis. Highly motivated to fix the problem, she saw several surgeons and sports medicine specialists. Ultimately, she had three options:

1. Inject artificial joint fluid (Synvisc) into the knee to temporarily restore function and reduce pain.

2. Undergo a total knee replacement and commit to three months of ongoing physical therapy.

3. Inject the knee with her own stem cells after undergoing an extensive surgical clean-out of the damaged cartilage and old scar tissue. The stem cells, sensing they were in a damaged but structurally intact knee, would then differentiate into fresh, new cartilage.

The patient's concierge physician helped her understand the ramifications of each choice. She ultimately selected the stem cell option. Because this procedure is cutting-edge, it varies widely in quality throughout the world. Additionally, it is not yet FDA-approved and thus is not available at most U.S. medical centers. The patient went to Europe for the procedure and received the therapy from the leading international stem cell expert and orthopedist.

To make this referral happen, her concierge physician researched the professional credentials and published research of the European stem cell expert. He made the referral and ensured that all medical records were summarized and transferred in advance of her visit. Postoperatively, the concierge physician and care team tracked her progress closely and facilitated appointments for her detailed physical therapy protocol. They also tracked the patient's progress throughout her recuperation. A follow-up MRI confirmed the establishment of new, intact knee cartilage. The patient made a full recovery, regained mobility, lost her pain and returned to the tennis court four months later.

For most of the Super Rich, the costs associated with world-class medical tourism are inconsequential. However, this is rarely the case for many other wealthy families. Thus, as we discussed in the previous chapter, a rising number of wealthy families are engaging financial professionals to provide wealth management solutions to deal with their possible future potential health care costs.

These costs are not insignificant. If you include the cost of travel (with family and support staff), lodging before and after the care event, and the pure cash cost of a cutting-edge surgical procedure or cancer therapy, the total bill can easily exceed a million dollars.

Creating an integrated plan that combines their personal predictive risk with an enduring plan to mitigate that risk is the optimal way to go for many families. Nevertheless, it still makes sense to plan for these identified risks, to look worldwide for the best care to address them and to put in place immediately the means to pay for them when needed.

Food for thought

Concierge medicine will likely dramatically expand as more physician and medical facilities, including hospitals, recognize the demand for concierge medicine and the value it provides patients. There's little doubt that many aspects of concierge medicine, such as leveraging personal technologies, will become normative. However, concierge medical practices will—generally speaking—continue to push the boundaries to deliver the gold standard in patient care.

Throughout this book, we have discussed the world of concierge medicine and asked you to think about the way concierge medicine would matter in your world. Now we'll revisit the question we asked back in Chapter 3:

Should you and your family become patients of a concierge medical practice?

By now, you have the information to answer this question confidently. Assuming your answer is yes, you need to decide which type of concierge medical practice would make the most sense for you and your loved ones. We'll help you make that decision in the next chapter.

CHAPTER 10

Selecting Your Concierge Medical Practice

We've found that the biggest challenge for many people in selecting a concierge medical practice is assessing the broad scope of quality among them, making it hard to judge which practices are really the best. There are no standardized rules for concierge practices, so you should be aware of the different possibilities and characteristics of each. You want to understand the various services that are available and how the different types of concierge medical practices compare.

The fundamental criteria

There are certain benchmark criteria associated with each type of concierge medical practice. Based on research with successful business owners, the Super Rich and single-family offices, the following is a partial list of key criteria for an exceptional connected care concierge medical practice:

Two days into a major PGA event, a touring pro hurt his hip climbing out of a steep bunker. Six hours later, his pain was severe enough to cause him to limp. His wife called their concierge medical practice where the physicians determined there was a distinct possibility of a ligamentous tear on the rim of the hip joint. An off-hours MRI of his hip was immediately arranged. The diagnosis was acute traumatic arthritis, but with no structural injury or tear. From his personal prescription medical kit and under the direct guidance of his concierge physician, he was started on a seven-day tapering course of prednisone. His concierge care team also arranged for in-hotel physical therapy at each tour stop. He made a smooth and relatively pain free recovery, staying on the course and finishing in the money.

- The practice must be totally committed to the care of its patients. If this is the core culture, it's then possible for everything else to work. The key dynamic here is that a great concierge medical practice makes medical care work for the patient, and not the patient work for the care.

- The professional skill and expertise of the physicians and support staff must be exemplary. Exceptionally high technical competencies are mandatory.

- Every member of the staff—especially the physicians—should have top-notch interpersonal skills. Poor communicators and those who fail to listen well should work elsewhere.

- Beyond any particular medical problem, the staff should have a broad and holistic understanding of each patient. This understanding goes well beyond just mastering the clinical information in a patient's records.

- The physicians of the concierge medical practice and all their related referral network specialists should be board-certified in their fields of practice.

- The staff should have a defined continuing medical education policy to ensure that everyone caring for patients is highly knowledgeable and broadly aware of the most recent clinically credible innovations.

- There should be no fiscal or professional conflicts of interest in the choice of specialist referrals, second opinions, diagnostic testing or treatments. The patient is entitled to the best care, wherever it might be found.

Your concierge medical practice

In addition to the fundamental criteria above, consider these personal factors when selecting a concierge medical practice:

- Your needs, wants and concerns

- What is available to you

- Your current state of health and its relative importance to your job and lifestyle

- How much you can travel and the value of your time

- What you are willing to pay

Next look at the services offered. In Chapter 4, we reviewed the various services generally available from many concierge medical practices. For each of the following services, determine how important it is for you and your family. Rate each one on a scale from extremely important to not important.

- 24/7, immediate on-call physicians

- Second opinion availability

- Complete case continuity

- Secure 24/7 access to medical records

- Longevity planning

- Access to leading specialists and medical centers

- Connected monitoring

- Tele-diagnosis and treatment

- Destination medical planning

- Foreign physician and hospital database

- Global medical evacuation

- Personal medical resources

With this information in hand, you can now determine which of the three basic types of concierge medical practices we discussed in Chapter 5 makes the most sense for your situation. Keep in mind that they are all operationally different.

You should also consider the three categories of health conditions we first discussed in Chapter 3: acute conditions, chronic conditions and longevity planning. In particular, weigh the appeal of the idea of living past 100. If a very long and healthy life is very meaningful to you, then you should focus on the types of concierge medical practices that provide state-of-the-art longevity planning.

Paying for concierge medicine

Another big factor in selecting a concierge medical practice is cost. Not only do you need to pay the concierge medical practice, but there also might be other costs, such as rehabilitation and cutting-edge treatments, that are not covered by insurance.

It's essential to realize that there are wide variations in cost, from an independent concierge physician charging a nominal monthly fee to an exclusive concierge physician and team charging millions of dollars annually. So you'll want to examine your financial resources and match them up to the specific concierge medical practices you feel are most appropriate.

As we discussed in Chapter 8, you might want to connect with a high-caliber wealth manager who can provide you with sophisticated strategies, such as captive insurance companies or private placement life insurance, that can help you deal with the costs of obtaining exceptional health care more effectively.

Becoming a patient of a concierge medical practice

Finally, consider the onboarding process of different types of practices. There are several different ways that most people join concierge medical practices. Often, the experience of joining a concierge medical practice depends on the state of the patient's health and current source of primary care. The best concierge medical practices will make the onboarding process as simple and seamless as possible, limiting the time the patient must devote to intake forms and medical record collection.

One common scenario is that a patient's current primary care physician transitions into a concierge practice model. The leader in transitioning traditional practices to a concierge model is MDVIP.

Another common concierge membership scenario is when a new patient joins a pre-existing concierge practice. In this scenario, the key part of the onboarding process is the collection of the patient's medical history. There is a tremendous range in the speed of this process across different concierge practices, and new patients may experience a wide range in the practices' commitment to their medical history.

Connected concierge practices have a different, highly streamlined patient enrollment process. This process varies based on the needs of the patient as he or she joins. Some patients are in the midst of a crisis or a new complex diagnosis, or are simply eager to increase the quality of their current health care.

For a nonurgent situation, the connected concierge process is fairly simple if the patient simply wants to switch from a conventional primary care physician and does not have any pressing health concerns. The patient will complete some comprehensive forms electronically. These forms will include medical history, allergies, past health care providers and, importantly, the depth of the patient's current level of care.

Once this information is entered into his or her electronic medical record, the patient is sent personal medical kits and has an orientation call to understand the kits and the app. As more medical records are received from other providers, the practice will collect, update and save all medical records electronically. The care team will use a best practices checklist to inform a physician of any issues for follow-up, like overdue tests, and schedule the follow-up accordingly.

Many patients choose a connected concierge practice just after they have received a serious diagnosis and the situation is relatively urgent. This is often the case with cancer or similar diseases. These patients are coming to the connected concierge medical practice because they want access to a broader network of experts and they know that they'll likely need even more continuous care in the future.

The onboarding process is similar for these patients, though it will also include immediate coordination with the concierge physician, all specialists involved and a series of specialist referrals.

Some patients come to connected concierge practices in a highly urgent manner, such as because of a life- or limb-threatening medical crisis. Frequently, they have been treated at a tertiary medical center and now need more medical resources to ensure an optimal outcome post-event. This is often the case for people who have had and been treated for a heart attack but now need someone who will guide them through recovery and a return to their original activities. These patients are usually worried about whom they will call if they have another crisis or their recovery goes off track in another way. Again, the primary motivation of these patients is a desire for rapid access and total continuity in their care.

In such a scenario, the patient is quickly enrolled and all relevant information is gathered from his or her current care providers. The concierge practice expedites the retrieval of the patient's medical records and creates an analysis of key metrics to be tracked and managed during recovery. Where applicable, the practice provides a personal smartphone monitor enabled to capture key metrics and creates a rules set to track and respond to changes in the key metrics. For the cardiac patient example described above, the patient would receive two smartphone devices: a blood pressure cuff and a cardiac rhythm monitor. The patient would also have calendared rechecks of biomarker blood tests, like LDL cholesterol, and an annual stress echocardiogram. This integrated approach, leveraging both personal connectivity and formal calendared biomarkers, would ensure a smooth and safe recovery.

Food for thought

With these factors in mind, you are now ready to answer one final question:

What type of concierge medical practice is optimal for you and your family?

As you make your decision, keep in mind that there are baseline standards—table stakes, if you will—that are associated with each type of concierge medical practice. Beyond fulfilling these fundamental criteria, any type of concierge medical practice you consider should be aligned with your personal criteria, including what you want and need, your current health status, and what you can afford. The range of services provided and the onboarding experience offered will also be important in your decision.

CHAPTER 11

Stepping into the World of Concierge Medicine

Our goal with this book was simple: to help you make better-informed decisions about taking part in the renaissance in health care now underway. To this end, we introduced you to concierge medicine: what it is, how you and your loved ones might benefit from it, how the various types of practices compare to one another, how the ultra-wealthy use it, and how astute wealth management can play a role in it.

By now, you've also considered a number of questions we've posed to help you clarify your priorities and possible next steps. Let these questions be your guide as you move forward into the world of concierge medicine.

First, assess your level of confidence in your ability to access high-quality health care in the future:

- Are you very confident that, going forward, you'll be able to access high-quality physicians when you need them?

- How confident are you that you'll be able to receive cutting-edge medical care?

- How confident are you that your physicians will be truly engaged and 100 percent committed to your well-being?

- How confident are you in getting the highest-quality medical care when you or your loved ones need it?

Now assess your most important priorities:

- What are your most precious assets?

- What are you doing to protect them?

Next, think about the range of services provided by the different types of concierge medical practices that we covered in Chapter 4 and how important each may—or may not be—to you and your family:

- Which of these myriad services are important to you?

- Which of these services do you consider essential?

- Which are "nice to have" but not critical?

Once you understand which services are most important to you, you're ready to answer these questions:

- Which version of concierge medicine do you find most appealing?

- What about that version do you think is essential and what is simply nice to have?

Now it's time to think bigger—and longer. Given the potential for extending human life spans, consider this:

- What are you doing about making sure you and your loved ones have long, healthy, active lives?

Given that money will very likely be a factor in your ultimate decision, think about these questions:

- How concerned are you about the costs of concierge medicine, cutting-edge medical diagnosis and treatment, and possibly running out of money because you are living past 100?

- If you are concerned about any of these issues, are you working with a high-caliber wealth manager who is knowledgeable about concierge medicine and can help you take steps to ensure—as best as possible—that you can afford the health care you want for yourself and your loved ones?

- If you have any doubts about getting the best financial advice, are you able to seek out a second opinion?

Finally, you're ready to answer the most important question:

- Should you and your family become patients of a concierge medical practice?

Assuming your answer is yes, consider one last question:

- What type of concierge medical practice is optimal for you and your family?

Stunning advances are being made every day in medical diagnoses and care. We see these advances continuing and even accelerating into the future, and believe that concierge medicine is the optimal route for accessing them. We wish you the best of success as you move forward in protecting your most precious asset: the health of you and your loved ones.

- Longevity Planning - protect most precious asset.